D1764768

Emerging Technological Risk

Stuart Anderson · Massimo Felici

Emerging Technological Risk

Underpinning the Risk of Technology Innovation

 Springer

Stuart Anderson
School of Informatics
The University of Edinburgh
Crichton Street 10
EH8 9AB Edinburgh
UK
e-mail: soa@staffmail.ed.ac.uk

Massimo Felici
School of Informatics
The University of Edinburgh
Crichton Street 10
EH8 9AB Edinburgh
UK
e-mail: mfelici@staffmail.ed.ac.uk

ISBN 978-1-4471-2142-8   e-ISBN 978-1-4471-2143-5
DOI 10.1007/978-1-4471-2143-5
Springer London Dordrecht Heidelberg New York

British Library Cataloguing in Publication Data
A catalogue record for this book is available from the British Library

Library of Congress Control Number: 2011940841

Cover design: eStudio Calamar S.L.

Printed on acid-free paper

Springer is part of Springer Science+Business Media (www.springer.com)

Foreword by Martyn Thomas

All engineers need a good understanding of risk, because uncontrolled risk threatens the success of all their engineering endeavours and the safety, security and quality of life of the people who operate, use or simply encounter the structures and systems that they develop. The proper recognition, analysis, mitigation and management of risks is therefore an ethical issue at the heart of professional engineering. In an increasingly complex society, risk is the subject of much democratic debate, whether it is the perceived or actual risk from genetically modified organisms, nuclear power stations, global warming, mobile phone base stations or the location of a landfill site. Yet, as many studies have shown, most citizens lack adequate knowledge or even good intuitions about the nature and relative size of risks from different sources. A better understanding of risk could reasonably be considered essential for effective democracy.

The research programme, *DIRC*, that spawned Anderson and Felici's book was a six-year, interdisciplinary research collaboration between computer scientists, sociologists, psychologists and ethnographers focussed on what makes complex systems dependable. When a system involves actions and interactions by and between people and machines, how can we have confidence that the system will deliver the desired outcomes (or even, as the minimum objective, avoid the worst outcomes)?

There are two classes of risk in any engineering project: (a) that the project will fail to deliver its objectives on time, within budgeted costs, or at all; and (b) that the delivered product or service will behave in undesired ways, causing problems, injury or damage. The two classes are closely related because, in attempting to meet time and cost constraints, errors of commission or omission may be made more likely. Conversely, if the product risks are inadequately managed then the development project will almost certainly overrun as problems become evident and cause delay and rework.

DIRC recognised that almost all computer-based systems are socio-technical and that it is essential to consider humans who interact with the computers as part of that larger socio-technical system. Human-Computer Interaction is therefore internal to the system rather than an external interface, and the capabilities and training of humans is part of system design and development.

This may seem obvious but it is widely overlooked. It is rare to see a Project Definition Document that adequately covers the work that will be required to design new business processes that use the new computer software, to train the users, to provide extra resources to support the periods of training and reduced productivity, to strengthen the helpdesk and so on. It is even rarer to find a risk register that covers the risks contained in these aspects of the system development and introduction. Yet these activities typically cost as much as the computer hardware and software, and often more.

Risk management can be seen as the most fundamental process in systems development because every other activity can be viewed as a task that mitigates a project risk. Of course, no project manager needs to carry out a risk analysis to discover that they need a project plan, adequate requirements capture, provision of accommodation and hardware, or acceptance criteria; yet if these or any other vital tasks are omitted, a competent risk analysis should identify the omission and lead to corrective action. Risk identification, analysis, mitigation and management are central to professional systems engineering, yet almost every risk register that I have seen is superficial and inadequate. A typical entry would read:

Risk	Probability	Impact	Mitigation	Mitigated probability
The user requirements are not adequately captured	High	High	Rigorous change management by Change Control Board	Low

This is useless, because the main feature of a weak specification is that it is interpreted differently by different people. A supplier will, quite reasonably, bid on the basis of the minimum work that is needed to do what the requirement says, in the context of what they know about their customer's business. The customer will often expect the new system to do at least what their old system did— probably enhanced by a few comments the salesman made about features he expected to be in the next release. The best outcome that both parties can hope for is that these disagreements will surface in the Change Control Board and that compromises will be made so, at best, the project costs and work will increase a bit rather than a lot. At worst, the project may fail. Neither outcome suggests that the risk has been mitigated or managed.

Project risks are real. They affect tangible things: effort, time, hardware and software costs, profitability and careers. I was an expert witness on one project to replace a Customer Information System that was not Y2K compliant. The inadequacies of an Output-Based Specification led to the selection of a replacement product and the underestimation of the modifications that would be required. The project overran and had to be installed with inadequate testing and some serious defects. The volume of customer calls about incorrect invoices swamped the call centre and very many calls went unanswered, so the customers stopped paying.

The company rapidly ran out of money and had to be rescued. All the Directors lost their jobs

Product risks are also real. In safety-critical systems, people could be injured or killed. Security breaches may allow personal data or commercial secrets to be copied. Products may have to be recalled and modified or replaced under warranty. Lawsuits are increasingly likely. Reputations may be lost and companies may lose market share or fail. Yet risk management may be inadequate even in safety-related work and there is an almost universal assumption that you can test a system and show that it is adequately safe, secure or reliable to be used in a critical application, even though this was proved to be untrue decades ago by Littlewood and Strigini, and Butler and Finelli.

Socio-technical systems have a wider range of risks. It is unacceptable to attribute an aircraft accident to 'pilot error' if the pilots behaved exactly as they had been trained to behave (for example because the flight simulator was wrong) or if their control interfaces made it easy to make a mistake and very difficult to detect the mistake once it had been made (perhaps by not displaying clearly the current flight modes of the aircraft control software). If you take a *DIRCish* approach to risk, you improve your chances of avoiding these pitfalls. If the pilots are inside your system boundary then so is the training simulator, which means that your hazard analysis should reveal that some aspects of the simulator are safety-critical and that these aspects must be developed with the appropriate care and scrutiny.

A DIRCish approach will start from the assumption that humans make mistakes, however well trained they are, and that the probability of mistakes under stress is high. A DIRCish approach will recognise that introducing systems that are intended to have only an advisory role will modify the behaviour of the humans that use them, with the possible outcome that the overall system will become less reliable rather than more. There can be no question that this book is needed. I hope that the insights that it contains will rapidly find their way into industrial practice.

May 2011   Dr. Martyn Thomas

Foreword by Cliff B Jones

It was my privilege to lead the *Interdisciplinary Research Collaboration* on Dependability of Computer-Based Systems and I am delighted to be able to set some context for this new book. DIRC, as it was known for short, was an exciting project that has helped change the way in which the development of computer-based systems is tackled. When we started the project at the very beginning of this century there was a strong temptation to separate technical problems of hardware and software dependability from the issues that manifest themselves when computer systems are inflicted on the inevitable human participants.

One should not be surprised at this split if one thinks back over the brief but startling history of computers: in their relatively short history, computers have developed from being physically huge and so expensive that only large organisations could countenance owning one to tiny items that occur in profusion in everyday purchases made by each of us. This development has seen a transition from a machine filling a room to which one delivered trays of punched cards—and received (much) later printouts—to devices that every one of us interacts with almost whatever task we wish to accomplish. Inevitably, this means that now the role of humans is crucial to all aspects of the system at large. This comment is especially appropriate for the dependability of the overall system: underestimating the role and expectations of users is a certain way to create a system whose overall dependability will be lamentable. The issues that need to be attended to go far beyond the—by no means unimportant—questions of HCI (Human-Computer Interaction). In fact, focusing on the equipment itself misses the dramatic changes that have been brought about by the scale of information to which hardware and software do no more than provide a portal. This book explores questions that must be considered such as reflecting in the system design the work patterns, expectations and responsibilities of the key participants whether they be medical staff, air traffic controllers or staff responsible for crucial financial systems.

As described in the Preface, the DIRC project adopted five "research themes" to which we wanted to make a long-term contribution: risk is one of these themes. Like all of its sibling themes, risk can be viewed from the point of view of humans and mechanisms. It is, for example, important to realise that most people are not overly rational when weighing up risks; they will for example blithely ignore automobile accident figures when they are in control of a car but react with horror when a train accident causes fatalities. Anyone who retains any doubt about the importance of the topic of risk must have somehow not noticed the enormous financial upheavals that have occurred in recent years. There is a large literature on risk which this book can help a reader navigate.

The DIRC project was exciting because of the way it brought together researchers from a range of disciplines. Interestingly the lead person in each of the five universities in the consortium had mainly technical backgrounds. I had, for example, spent many years undertaking research on how to reason about the conformance of a programme to its formal specification. It should be obvious that to describe precisely what a programme should do and then accept an offering that fails to do what was prescribed is likely to be one source of failure in the dependability of the overall system of which the program is a part; but it must be equally obvious that getting a specification (however precise) that ignores aspects of the human players in the overall system is another route to disaster. There is no need to debate which is 'more important'—both aspects are crucial.

Getting interdisciplinary teams to cooperate is itself a task that needs thought. Coincidentally, an early part of my own career was focused on operations research and I remembered the excitement of working with mathematicians and chemists to solve problems in oil refining. DIRC experienced the same rush of cooperation when we got some real problems in front of us. In my opinion, this is the only way to rise above sterile debates about terminology and methodological prejudices: present a team with a challenge such as understanding the role of computer tools in increasing the reliability of the reading of medical images and progress quickly follows.

This comment presents the opportunity to acknowledge the many colleagues (well over fifty) who committed significant slices of their research efforts to our six year endeavour. The contributions of some of these colleagues are represented in this book—many more names are listed on the DIRC web site (www.dirc.org.uk). Each of them took a risk. At a minimum, a researcher's publication rate takes a hit when he or she tries to merge their contribution into an interdisciplinary effort. Many also experienced the conservative attitudes of journal editors and project reviewers when they came to publish their work or apply for new grants. But I believe that it was for all in DIRC a career changing experience—and at times super fun! I should also like to say a special word of thanks to Martyn Thomas who freely gave his time and wisdom both to chair the advisory committee and, sometimes, to listen to the doubts of a project director.

We could not, of course, have undertaken the project without the IRC funding from the UK EPSRC. In particular, flexible funding extending over more than six years was essential to get, often young, researchers to take the risks outlined above. We are equally grateful to the varied organisations that let us get involved in their projects. These involvements ranged from quick glimpses through to the opportunity to undertake longitudinal studies over many years.

To all potential readers of this book, I should say that DIRCish studies can open their eyes to essential concerns that can help them reduce the risk and/or pain of any systems they are in a position to develop.

May 2011   Prof. Cliff B Jones

Preface

Society is increasingly reliant on complex computer-based systems ranging from control systems in aircraft, trains and cars to business critical systems such as e-banking systems to systems that are an integral part of our critical national infrastructures. These systems have to be dependable—failures can have serious consequences, e.g. loss of life, loss of essential services or significant financial losses. Despite much progress having been made in technical approaches to achieving dependability—there is still a long way to go—many failures arise through the interactions of organisations, people and computer systems. It is possible to tackle these problems and make significant steps forward in improving dependability through an interdisciplinary approach.

This book draws on the *Interdisciplinary Research Collaboration in Dependability*—the DIRC project—a truly multidisciplinary project, bringing together researchers with backgrounds in computer science, mathematics, psychology, sociology and business. It involved researchers with an interest in dependable socio-technical systems from the Universities of Newcastle, York, Lancaster, Edinburgh and City University London. The long-term (six-year) research project supported the development of knowledge, methods and tools that enhance our understanding of socio-technical system dependability and support developers of dependable systems. This made remarkable progress across a number of areas. The interdisciplinary contribution has been increasingly recognised as an important insights into dependability research.

Interdisciplinary Research Themes

Interdisciplinary Research Themes within the DIRC project acted as a way of gathering, analysing and recording the lasting knowledge come out of research carried out during the collaboration. One of the motivations in selecting the themes was that it is possible (and interesting) to look at them from both a technical (system) and human (user) viewpoint. Furthermore, in order to progress on difficult research themes, it is necessary to be able to deploy ideas, e.g. from the psychological or sociological research to the technical issues (and, of course, vice versa). The Interdisciplinary Research Collaboration in Dependability identified five major research themes: *Structure, Diversity, Timeliness, Responsibility* and *Risk*.

The structure of a system can contribute to its dependability, understandability and its ability to evolve. The *Structure* research theme studied the structure of both human organisations and technical systems (and the way they interact). An essential element of dependability is protective redundancy, or fault tolerance. But the risk of common-mode failures among redundant elements needs to be contained by actively pursuing diversity. The *Diversity* theme studied the advantages and difficulties of pursuing diversity both in systems and processes, including the socio-technical processes that develop technical and socio-technical systems. The work included empirical studies as well as probabilistic modelling.

Another characteristic of socio-technical systems is that they are required to function at many different time scales (from microseconds or less to hours or more). Time is clearly a crucial notion in the specification (or behavioural description) of socio-technical systems, but it has a wide range of technical, social and psychological properties. The *Timeliness* theme explored this rich set of issues.

The *Responsibility* theme explored one of the major differences between people and computers—people can be given or assume responsibilities. Many system failures are, at least partly, a consequence of responsibility failures. To reduce responsibility-related failures, it is necessary to develop a deeper understanding of these failures, to understand how responsibilities interact in complex socio-technical systems and to invent ways of making responsibilities explicit in models that can be used to inform system design.

Risk in socio-technical systems is more heterogeneous and difficult to capture than in conventional systems. This is due to the fact that socio-technical systems are deeply embedded in social and organisational contexts. The *Risk* theme emphasised the need to consider issues of risk perception since different participants in an organisation have very different views of the existence and severity of hazards. It is also important to consider mechanisms for handling risk arising from the ongoing process of change in organisational systems. This book draws on the research results contributing to the Risk theme.

Book Overview

Socio-technical systems carry a degree of risk. The traditional view is that risk relates to faults in systems. Risk management usually relies on the frequency of manifestation and severity of the consequences of system flaws. Socio-technical systems are deeply embedded in organisations. Hence, understanding risks associated with such systems is difficult and exposes the limitation of traditional approaches to risk. Organisations comprise many different groups, whose risk perception may differ radically and whose needs for and attitude to system change also varies depending on role and environment. Thus, we have undertaken two important lines of work in the Risk theme: exploiting the Social Science literature (e.g. on risk perception) to highlight and to help manage socio-technical risk in complex organisations, and managing the risk of change in complex socio-technical systems. For instance, Social Science literature on Cultural Theory demonstrates how different constitutions of social groupings within organisations shape risk perception. We have, therefore, analysed potential risks in different organisations focusing on how the dominance of particular groups de-emphasises certain classes of risk. Our analysis provides the basis for a technique, complementing traditional approaches to risk, for identifying *emerging technological risk*. This is an outline of an *Interdisciplinary Risk Reader*. A multidisciplinary overview of risk motivates the approach to studying risk in an interdisciplinary fashion covering things such as the role of empirical studies, the extent to which theory is useful, how theories from one discipline inform work in others ones. The introduction motivates the selection of the studies and draws out some of the common concepts across the studies.

Case Studies

We have conducted several case studies in diverse domains in order to generalise and combine theories together with empirical findings into a comprehensive account of socio-technical risk. For example, in a large-scale study of dependable process transfer from one location to another, we discovered that the structure and modularity of organisations can pose significant risks for organisations. In particular, the loss of information across organisational boundaries can expose complex organisations to significant risks. In studying change, we have been particularly interested in exploring hybrid socio-technical approaches to mitigate the risk of change in complex organisations. Emerging evolutionary structures define technology trajectories, which characterise system evolution as the result of social negotiation processes. Our studies highlight how responsibility and trust are critical aspects affecting work practices as well as technological innovation. Misunderstanding responsibility and developing mistrust expose organisations to technological risk. We have, then, studied the role of trust in managing risk and as a potential source of risk arising from system failures or mistrust. At a macroscopic scale, a fascinating example of risk in large systems is drawn from the domain of economics. Our studies take into account lessons drawn from market mechanisms for the construction of large-scale socio-technical systems. The innovative use of a mathematical model, in particular for hedge funds, explores the connection between diversity in computer systems and diversity of portfolio together with social mechanisms that defeat attempts to maintain diversity in a changing market. Finally, we have extensively investigated different medical domains, which provided various accounts of complex socio-technical settings. The investigations of various medical settings allowed us to generalise common findings across different domains.

Risk Underpinnings

Our studies identify a set of socio-technical risk underpinnings, namely, *Boundary Hazards, Evolutionary Hazards and Performativity Hazards*. In this book we choose to focus on these three classes because they provide a characterisation of newly emerging technological risk in complex organisations that make extensive use of socio-technical systems. These underpinnings have their origins in and take into account multidisciplinary aspects of risk.

For example, *Boundary Hazards* arise at inter-, or intra-organisational boundaries. At organisational boundaries, different strategies are possible, in some situations attempts are made to establish a formal interface, in others the situation is so chaotic that internal structures require external scrutiny. Organisations are exposed to Boundary Hazards and consequently to risk. Boundary Objects arise as a key element in analysing complex organisations. For us, boundary objects are often a starting point for the analysis of Boundary Hazards.

A good example of a boundary object is a classification system, or simply classification. Classifications pervade organisations and capture agreed interpretations of action and information in organisations. They are the result of technical as well as political struggles addressed over the years. Classifications arise both locally as a result of bottom-up attempts to make sense of the organisation and globally in a top-down adoption of standards. In complex organisations, classifications are continually being reinterpreted in order to support intra-group working and to support inter-group interaction.

The process of developing classifications or adopting standard classifications differs across different communities of practice in an organisation. Interfaces between different communities of practice often give rise to knowledge, structured by classifications or standards, the interpretation of the shared knowledge by different communities of practice is critical to the operation of the organisation.

Classifications provide a structure for information, but its interpretation will depend on the mechanisms that shape the structure and the policies and practices of the communities involved in shaping the classification. The detailed processes involved in shaping and adopting classifications and standards give rise to risk, particularly in how information codified in a particular classification is interpreted in different communities of practice that share the codified information. Boundary hazards have potentially critical consequences for the activities of the organisation.

Our case studies analyse problems of working with and evolving classifications. These concerns are central to the organisational objectives of technology innovation in complex organisations. The studies allow us to reflect on the methodological implications of addressing the design and evolution of organisational technology innovations.

Technological risk arising from organisational technology innovation relates to uncertainty in engineering design knowledge with respect to technical, organisational and environmental factors. This uncertainty in engineering design knowledge represents a source of risk.

Discrepancies between standard schemes and local practices (rooted in existing heterogeneous information structures and practices) mean that the introduction of standardisation which can yield a sense of increasing general accountability, scrutiny and control over distant activities may also be accompanied by a loss of local focus and detail oversight. This can be a source of socio-technical undependabilities. The contradictory effects of standardisation efforts go to the heart of questions of trust and in particular the notion that standardised information structures and practices can resolve the problems of trust in complex and (spatially and culturally) dispersed organisational settings.

Emerging Technological Risk

Our case studies allow us to identify a set of risk underpinnings, or socio-technical hazards, which we can generalise across different application domains. These findings form the basis for guidelines complementing and extending traditional approaches to risk. The guidelines benefit from our multidisciplinary, eventually interdisciplinary, approach to risk. The extensive investigations of diverse medical case studies provided an application domain into which we could generalise and assess our findings. The empirical, as well as theoretical, nature of our work is such that other industry domains may benefit from our research findings.

Interdisciplinary Risk Reader

The original idea of this book was to collect a set of multidisciplinary literature that contributes towards the advancements of an interdisciplinary account of emerging technological risk. This gave rise to an *Interdisciplinary Risk Reader—* nicknamed within the DIRC project as—*the DIRC Risk Reader, the Risk Reader of the Interdisciplinary Research Collaboration in Dependability.* This book is, therefore, aimed at a multidisciplinary audience of researchers and practitioners, who would find benefits from learning about diverse perspectives on technology risk. Although many different books address technological risk, it is very difficult to find any guidance in understanding and assimilating diverse literature drawn from different backgrounds. This book represents a step towards bridging diverse contributions in order to sustain a fruitful debate about *emerging technological risk.*

Edinburgh, May 2011   Stuart Anderson
                                                                       Massimo Felici

Acknowledgments

This book would have been impossible without the contributions of our colleagues. We hope that this book gives suitable credits to their work.We would also like to acknowledge the UK Engineering and Physical Sciences Research Council (EPSRC) for the funding of the Interdisciplinary Research Collaboration in Dependability—the DIRC project, grant GR/N13999—which allowed us to work over a long-term project outside the constraints that short-term research projects usually impose. This book has also received support in part by the Interdisciplinary Design and Evaluation of Dependability—the INDEED project, grant EP/E001297/1—which allowed us to extend and consolidate our work on risk and trust.

Contents

Part I   Introduction

1   Risks, Technologies and Societies 3
 1.1   Multidisciplinary Perspectives on Risk................... 3
 1.2   Technology Risk...................................... 5
 1.3   Risk in Engineering Knowledge 9
  1.3.1   Knowledge Uncertainty 10
  1.3.2   Knowledge Negotiation 11
  1.3.3   Knowledge Granularity 13
 1.4   Human Dimensions of Technology Risk................. 15
 1.5   Risk Society.. 16
 1.6   Interdisciplinary Technological Risk 22
 References 24

Part II   Risk Underpinnings

2   Unbounded Technology 31
 2.1   Classification Systems and Boundary Objects 31
 2.2   Patterns of Boundary Infrastructures 34
  2.2.1   Standardisation 36
  2.2.2   Adopting Generic Technology 39
  2.2.3   Creating Organisational Infrastructures 42
 2.3   Boundary Hazards................................... 47
  2.3.1   Addressing Boundary Hazards 49
 References 50

3   Technological Evolution   53
   3.1   Evolutionary Observations   53
   3.2   Evolving Practices   56
          3.2.1   Understanding Responsibility   58
          3.2.2   Acquiring Trust   59
          3.2.3   Dependability Knowledge   60
   3.3   Technology Trajectories   61
          3.3.1   Requirements Evolution   63
          3.3.2   Structuring Evolution   64
          3.3.3   Engineering Knowledge Growth   66
          3.3.4   Evolutionary Dependencies   68
   3.4   Judging Moving Targets   71
          3.4.1   Constructing Arguments   71
          3.4.2   Reusing Arguments   73
          3.4.3   Changing Arguments   75
   3.5   Evolutionary Hazards   77
          3.5.1   Addressing Evolutionary Hazards   78
   References   81

4   Social Connectivity   85
   4.1   Social Accounts of Technologies   85
   4.2   System Performativity   87
          4.2.1   Emerging Social Networks   89
          4.2.2   Emerging Social Behaviour   91
   4.3   Performativity Hazards   93
          4.3.1   Addressing Performativity Hazards   94
   References   95

Part III   Emerging Technological Risk

5   Hardening Social Links   99
   5.1   Complex Socio-Technical Settings   99
   5.2   Organisational Knowledge   100
          5.2.1   Knowledge Management   101
          5.2.2   Knowledge Embedding   102
   5.3   Technology Interaction   104
          5.3.1   Knowledge Rationality   105
          5.3.2   Knowledge Timing   108
   5.4   Technology Communities   111
          5.4.1   Enabling Technologies   111
          5.4.2   Mediating Technologies   112
   5.5   Hardening Social Links   113
   References   113

Part IV Conclusions

6 Emerging Technological Risk 119
   6.1 Underpinning Technological Risk 119
   6.2 Classes of Socio-Technical Hazards. 121
       6.2.1 Boundary Hazards. 121
       6.2.2 Evolutionary Hazards 122
       6.2.3 Performativity Hazards 123
       6.2.4 Addressing Emerging Technological Risk 124
   References 125

Annotated Bibliography. 127

Further Reading 175

Author Index 177

Subject Index 181

Abbreviations

AC	Alternating Current
ACM	Association for Computing Machinery
ADLs	Activities of Daily Living
ALARP	As Low As Reasonably Possible
ANT	Actor-Network Theory
ATC	Air Traffic Control
ATM	Air Traffic Management
CAD	Computer Aided Detection
CBOE	Chicago Board Options Exchange
CDO	Collateralized Debt Obligation
COTS	Commercial-Off-The-Shelf
CR_C	Cumulative Number of Requirements Changes
CSCW	Computer-Supported Collaborative Work or Computer Supported Cooperative Work
CT	Cultural Theory
DEPOSE	Design, Equipment, Procedures, Operators, Supplies and materials, and Environment
DIRC	Interdisciplinary Research Collaboration in Dependability
DOPE	Displacement of the ETT; Obstruction of the ETT; Pneumothorax; and Equipment malfunction
EMR	Electronic Medical Record
ETT	Endo-Tracheal Tube
GTH	Generic Types of Harm
HAZOP	Hazard and Operability Analysis
HCI	Human-Computer Interaction
HMI	Human-Machine Interaction
HRA	Human Reliability Analysis
HRMI	Historical Requirements Maturity Index
HSE	Health & Safety Executive
HSL	Health & Safety Laboratory
ICD	International Classification of Diseases

ICT	Information and Communication Technology
IS	Information Society
IT	Information Technology
LTCM	Long-Term Capital Management
MIS	Management Information System
NAT	Normal Accident Theory
NICU	Neonatal Intensive Care Unit
PIMS	Patient Information Management System
RMI	Requirements Maturity Index
RSI	Requirements Stability Index
SCA	Software Criticality Analysis
SHEL	Software, Hardware, Environment, Liveware
SML	Short Mortality List
SRS	Software Requirements Specification
SST	Social Shaping of Technology
WHO	World Health Organization
WHO-FIC	WHO Family of International Classifications
XML	Extensible Markup Language

Part I
Introduction

Chapter 1
Risks, Technologies and Societies

Technological risk arises when some technical artefact is deployed in a situation where its operation can result in adverse consequences. Risk is a an intensively studied phenomenon across a wide range of disciplines and each discipline brings a particular, distinctive, focus. Academic work on risk is often either retrospective, looking at a particular incident, or abstract, considering general properties of the phenomenon. The context of this book is to consider how such work on risk can contribute to the prospective practice of understanding risk as a system is designed and deployed. In this context no particular aspect of the artefact has been 'topicalised' by an incident and so our goal is not the deep analysis of a single feature but rather to achieve a balanced view of risk arising from deployment and operation of technological artefacts. Our key to achieving this is the *diversity* of perspectives on risk across many disciplines. By considering several perspectives we arrive at a composite view that challenges the applicability and effectiveness of purely technological risk analysis (as distinct from organisational risk analysis). This chapter highlights different perspectives that contribute towards an interdisciplinary account of *emerging technological risk*. We review accounts of risk that emphasise different granularity of analysis and different processes engaged in realising such risks. We consider relationships between studies of risk that point to an emerging holistic account of technological risk. This chapter suggests how future research and practice can contribute to a deeper, interdisciplinary, understanding of technological risk.

1.1 Multidisciplinary Perspectives on Risk

Research on technology risk exhibits huge variation in emphasis and this ranges along several dimensions. Two of the most critical dimensions are scale (from micro to macro), and the focus for the production and control of risk (from artefact-focused to culturally focused). Each discipline also brings a particular perspective that prioritises some collections of features over others. At first sight these perspectives might appear to be incompatible and difficult to reconcile. Here we provide a categorisation

S. Anderson and M. Felici, *Emerging Technological Risk*,
DOI: 10.1007/978-1-4471-2143-5_1, © Springer-Verlag London Limited 2012

of a range of work we have found useful for analysing and controlling risk in complex socio-technical systems. Constructing such a categorisation requires us to strike a difficult balance between being fully faithful to the literature and providing a structure that can facilitate the analysis and control of technology risk in socio-technical systems. We could construct a complex three-dimensional categorisation having scale, focus and disciplinary perspective as the dimensions but this would result in an array of categories, many of which would be underpopulated. Instead we have simplified the categorisation by conflating all three dimensions and considering the following points on our single dimension: technical (small-scale, technical analysis), engineering (medium-scale, engineering analysis), managerial (medium-scale, managerial/human analysis), and social (large-scale, social/cultural analysis). This categorisation is open to criticism but we have taken a pragmatic choice that allows us to understand some important aspects of the complexity of a full account of risk in technology. Coming to a better understanding of the nature of *risk in technology* requires us to uncover this complexity in order to refine our approach to technological risk. We highlight how accounts of technological risk relate to each other. Understanding technology risks and how they relate to each other enhances our ability to structure and perform risk analysis at different levels of granularity. Our simplifying assumption is that accounts of technological risk cluster at different levels of analysis and these levels of analysis focus on particular aspects of systems and processes that generate risk.

Here we provide an analysis that highlights similarities that account for important categories of technological risks in complex settings. This chapter enhances our understanding of technological risk by reviewing different accounts from a range of disciplines. We contribute to the development of a multidisciplinary (or interdisciplinary[1]) perspective by reviewing work from a range of disciplines, highlighting similarities and constructing a categorisation of accounts of risk with a particular emphasis on technological risk. The goal of this chapter is to provide a preliminary analysis of diverse aspects contributing towards *multidisciplinary accounts of risk* that provides a context for the remaining chapters of the book [10].

This chapter identifies key elements of risk that contribute towards an interdisciplinary account of *emerging technological risk*. On the one hand, it extends and complements engineering accounts of technological risk. On the other hand, it overcomes the limitations of a single disciplinary perspective. It encourages and stresses bridges between, for instance, social and engineering accounts of technological risk. Moreover, it makes social dimensions of risk accessible to practitioners, and vice

---

[1] The work in [54] questions the nature of *interdisciplinarity* as well as to *multidisciplinarity*. Multidisciplinary work often faces difficulties in practice. However, this book stresses how multidisciplinary work is a potential strategy for overcoming limitations 'within' single disciplines. The adaptation of artefacts (e.g. models, concepts) drawn from other disciplines into an integrated framework supports the seeking of understanding complex problems, which remain unresolved or incomprehensible within single disciplines. This allows us to tackle complex, otherwise unresolved or incomprehensible, problems into emerging 'interdisciplinary' accounts, which characterise 'solutions' into an integrated framework arising from diverse disciplines and filling knowledge gaps within and between disciplines.

versa. Linking diverse accounts and relevant work on risk of technology innovation enhances our ability to analyse and to explain risk issues. It provides ways of interrogating technology innovation from a range of disciplinary perspectives on risk. It is possible to identify a wide spectrum of technological risk, from the technical to the social. The main categories of accounts of risk identified in this chapter are: *technology risk, risk in engineering knowledge, human dimensions of technology risk* and *risk society*. This simple categorisation provides a good starting point for a richer account of risk in technology.

1.2 Technology Risk

Computer related risks originate in various system engineering processes (e.g. system development, operation and use) [47, 59]. The study of system features like reliability and safety has contributed to the advance of engineering methodologies that address potential risks [47]. The main computer related risks fall into two main categories of sources of problems [47]: *system development* (e.g. requirements definition, hardware and software implementations, evolution) and *system operation and use* (e.g. natural environmental factors, infrastructural factors, software misbehaviour, human limitations in system use). These categories are defined principally from a technical viewpoint. Engineering methodologies, in particular in the safety-critical domain [38, 57], address some of these risks, although they provide limited means to understand and identify subtle emerging risks (e.g. socio-technical risks). For example, IEC 61508, one of the principal safety-critical software standards, takes the software architecture of the systems as the organising structure for the analysis of the safety of the system. This prioritises software architecture as the main origin of potential failure and the main means to manage failure [33].

From an engineering viewpoint, it is useful to distinguish between a *hazard*—"a state or set of conditions of a system (or an object) that, together with other conditions in the environment of the system (or object), will lead inevitably to an accident (loss event)" [38]—and its associated *risk*—"the hazard level combined with (1) the likelihood of the hazard leading to an accident (sometimes called danger) and (2) hazard exposure or duration (sometime called latency)" [38]. These definitions of hazard and risk together with the notions of system and environment are the bases of causal analysis of accident investigations [34, 38, 57].

In safety-critical domains the focus is on *failures* in the engineering of computer systems whose consequences lead to loss or injury [38]. This focus on the consequences of failure clarifies the distinction between safety (i.e. a concern over loss or injury) and reliability (i.e. a concern that the system can be relied on to function predictably) properties of systems. Our increasing dependence on software, more generally on novel system components that often contain embedded software, has stimulated a growing interest in justifying *confidence* in system properties for systems containing novel components [32, 44]. This has provided the stimulus for research and practice addressing system *dependability* [8, 11].

The nature of system dependability and how to address dependability-related system issues are still the subject of ongoing debate and research [11]:

> The original definition of dependability is the ability to deliver service that can justifiably be trusted. This definition stresses the need for justification of trust in services. The alternate definition that provides the criterion for deciding if the service is dependable is the dependability of a system is the ability to avoid service failures that are more frequent and more severe than is acceptable.

Dependability attributes: *availability*, *reliability*, *safety*, *confidentiality*, *integrity* and *maintainability* refine overall dependability into complementary properties that can be analysed independently to some extent. In dependability, *impairments* define how *faults* (i.e. the initial cause) cause *errors* (i.e. system states that are identifiably erroneous) that may lead to system *failures* (i.e. deviance from the expected system service). This identifies a causal chain (i.e. ..., fault, error, failure, ...) by which system failures emerge. Note that it is possible to give slightly, but fundamentally, different interpretations to these mechanisms. These interpretations of the impairments and their mutual relationships highlight a different view of causal relationships (e.g. ..., error, fault, failure, ...) [38]. Organisational culture is the locus for variations in interpretation of impairments and uncovering underlying assumptions in organisational culture is critical for assessing system dependability. The *means* for dependability are the methods or techniques that enhance the system ability to deliver the desired service and to place trust in this ability.

Research in dependability has contributed to the development of various methodologies "to specify, design, implement and exploit systems where faults are natural, expected and tolerable" [8]. Unfortunately, technical arguments for system dependability are often insufficient to take into account the socio-technical issues that shape how the broader design, implementation and operational environments are structured and how the surrounding structures provide varying interpretive contexts within which a system operates.

The origins of work on dependability are in the analysis of specific *accidents* that have been sufficiently serious to raise concern. This history is witness to the capacity of a single accident to support many, often conflicting, accounts of the locus and causal connections that surround a particular accident. This focus on system *accidents* highlights features that characterise technology risk. For example, distinguishing between *accidents* and *incidents* depends on the severity and affected system parts [49]:

> An accident is a failure in a subsystem, or the system as a whole, that damages more than one unit and in doing so disrupts the ongoing or future output of the system. An incident involves damage that is limited to parts or a unit, whether the failure disrupts the system or not.

This distinction between accident and incident and the assumptions underlying the distinction have often contributed to the debate and comparison of relevant theories of risk [34, 38], in particular, the contrast between *Normal Accident Theory* (NAT) and *High Reliability Theory* (HRT) [49]:

> The fundamental difference between Normal Accident Theory and High Reliability Theory (HRT) is that HRT believes that if only we try harder we will have virtually accident-free systems even if they are complexly interactive and tightly coupled, while NAT believes that no matter how hard we try we will still have accidents because of intrinsic characteristics of complex/coupled systems.

The HRT view is that with appropriate structure and resources any incident can be contained within a unity and need not propagate to cause an accident. In [49] Perrow introduces the concepts of *complexity* and *coupling* in order to provide a framework for the analysis of system risks based on characteristics of the technical artefacts and organisational structures of systems. The framework classifies organisational systems, or DEPOSE systems (consisting of the following components: design, equipment, procedures, operators, supplies and materials, and environment), according to complexity of interaction (i.e. *linear interactions* or *complex interactions*) and *coupling* (i.e. loose or tight) between components [49]. Complex systems, according to Perrow's classification, are those exhibiting complex interactions, where "linear interactions are those in expected and familiar production or maintained sequence, and those that are quite visible even if unplanned", whereas, "complex interactions are those of unfamiliar sequences, or unplanned and unexpected sequences, and either not visible or not immediately comprehensible" [49]. The classification highlights three main classes of high-risk systems depending on the severity and complexity of risks, as well as the possibility of effectively addressing those risks [49]:

> The first would be the systems that are hopeless and should be abandoned because the inevitable risks outweigh any reasonable benefits [...]; the second, systems that we are either

unlikely to be able to do without but which could be made less risky with considerable effort [...], or where the expected benefits are so substantial that some risks should be run, but not as many as we are now running [...]; the third group includes those systems which, while hardly self-correcting in all respects, are self-correcting to some degree and could be further improved with modest efforts [...].

Perrow sees high-complexity/high-coupling situations as the hopeless case where accidents would be the norm. Highly coupled situations (e.g. power grids) comprise his second class and high-complexity situations are the third class. This classification according to the complexity/coupling framework is in agreement with technically informed risk analysis, although *social and cultural rationality* can result in different *risk perception* [29, 49, 55] depending on social and cultural structure that results in different interpretations of risk classifications. In order to explaining disagreements in risk assessment, Perrow identifies three rationalities [49]: *absolute rationality*, of informed and knowledgeable people (e.g. economists and engineers), *bounded or limited rationality*, emerging in risk analysis as human reasoning on knowledge, and *social and cultural rationality*, in which anyone is involved due to belonging to the society. For example, different cultural structures interpret the risks associated with nuclear power stations in different ways. Even within a single culture perceptions can vary over time. For example, the rise in concern over climate change has seen some reinterpretation of the risk associated with nuclear power but accidents at nuclear plants can further complicate how cultural concerns are articulated.

Although we might hope that we might be able to assess the risks associated with a particular situation in a absolutely rational manner we are always left with a complex mix of bounded, social and cultural rationality because producing additional knowledge has a cost and resource is limited and social and cultural features pervade the production of new knowledge. Thus, uncertainty always affects the reasoning of experts and the informed observer as well as the general public. Uncertainty is the ground on which social and cultural rationality flourishes. Dread and uncertainty surround many of the judgements taken in risk assessment, for example, predicting the long-term implications for future generations of a particular decision taken now. Although the coupling/complexity risk classification takes into account victims[2] of system risks, there is always uncertainty surrounding the consequences of particular decisions. There are three main clusters of interrelated social judgement associated with uncertainty [49]: *dread risk* (e.g. lack of control over the activity, high catastrophic potential), *unknown risk* (e.g. unknown, new, delayed) and *societal and personal exposure*. Often this aspect of social and cultural rationality seeks to re-prioritise risk classification and identification driven by concerns over uncertainty. Some of these aspects of risk perception can be mitigated by general policies, for

---

[2] The complexity/coupling framework considers four types of victims depending on the direct exposures to system failures [49]. These types fall in the following categories: *first-party victims* involving system operators, *second-party victims* directly associated with the system (e.g. as suppliers or users) but without influence over it, *third-party victims* are accidentally involved in system failures, and *fourth-party victims* involving future generations exposed, mostly, to environmental and contamination hazards (e.g. radiation and toxic chemicals).

example: centralisation or decentralisation of control, clearly defining authority and responsibility.

The role of uncertainty and the production of knowledge about a technical system and its organisational setting are critical in both sourcing information on which to base judgements and in illustrating the diversity of interpretations that can be given to the available knowledge. In the case of systems with tightly coupled components exhibiting complex interactions [49] the potential diversity of behaviour means that we find it very difficult to generate enough knowledge about the situation to make informed decisions thus social and cultural rationality will always play an important role in assessing risk in such systems. The next section considers how we go about creating engineering knowledge in the context of innovative systems where the role of uncertainty is particularly prominent.

1.3 Risk in Engineering Knowledge

The thesis, proposed by Vincenti, that we view *Engineering as Knowledge* [58] has been investigated and validated in various engineering domains. The history of engineering highlights activities that contribute to the acquisition (and loss) of knowledge about technical systems. Taking the technical artefact as the primary element we see that technical systems embody engineering knowledge that we can access to a greater or lesser extent and that knowledge is current to a greater or lesser extent. Accessing knowledge will require a mixture of observing the system in operation, testing the system, inspecting software and reading documentation that may or may not be up to date. Taking the artefact as primary makes a clear distinction between engineering and applied science because engineering involves design innovation and the creation of technical artefacts. In contrast, the view of engineering purely from a knowledge perspective reduces engineering to creating designs that take into account the available engineering knowledge.

Vincenti emphasises the broader view of engineering knowledge that is concerned with the artefact and its operating environment that distinguishes engineering from applied science. Within this broad conception of engineering activity he identifies two different types of designs: *normal design* and *radical design*. *Normal design* is the design of "normal technology" based on "what technological communities usually do" [58]. This is characterised by relatively low levels of uncertainty and by a very low need for innovation in the design processes needed to create the design. *Radical design*, as distinct from normal design, involves the design of technology under quite significant *knowledge uncertainty* [58] and may require significant innovation in the design process to create the required technology.

1.3.1 Knowledge Uncertainty

Vincenti stresses that engineering is a learning process [58] particularly in the case of radical design but even normal design may require some process innovation. The *engineering learning process* involves (seven) interacting elements (e.g. familiarisation with the problem, development of instruments and techniques, measurement of characteristics, assessment of results) that form a complex epistemic structure. There is no simple linear relationship between the interacting elements of the engineering learning process. Engineering, especially in the case of radical design, follows an accidentally iterative *variation-selection model* for the growth of knowledge.[3] The variation-selection model involves three main cognitive activities that characterise the growth processes of engineering knowledge:

- *Searching of past similar experiences* where engineering knowledge was successfully (and unsuccessfully) used. Looking at success and failure helps identify the range of applicability of forms of engineering knowledge [50, 51].
- *Incorporating innovation features* into artefacts highlights two features of engineering knowledge: (a) engineering knowledge arises from communities of practice adopting (or naturalising) knowledge into artefacts, and (b) as *distributed cognition* [48] where a community of users reach some (conditional) agreement on how to use artefacts.
- *Selecting design alternatives* by identifying key selection criteria in the environment and communities of use and deploying these criteria to select design alternatives that are most likely to work.

Vincenti's account of Engineering knowledge identifies various categories of knowledge [58]: *Fundamental design concepts, Criteria and specifications, Theoretical tools, Auantitative data, Practical considerations* and *Design instrumentalities.* For Vincenti these categories cover engineering knowledge[4] consisting of *descriptive knowledge, prescriptive knowledge* and *tacit knowledge* contributing towards *explicit knowledge* or *procedural knowledge* where the knowledge is not explicitly available but rather is packaged as "correct procedure" that should be followed. It is clear that it may be difficult or impossible correctly to identify explicit knowledge that underpins procedural knowledge and that there may be considerable choice in mapping from procedural knowledge to explicit knowledge.

---

[3] Different activities contribute towards generating engineering knowledge. In distinguishing between science and engineering, Vincenti in [58] identifies the main activities (i.e. *Transfer from science, Invention, Theoretical engineering research, Experimental engineering research, Design practice, Production, Direct trial*) generating engineering knowledge.

[4] Differentiating knowledge according to its purpose highlights different types—"Descriptive knowledge, as the term suggests, describes things as they are. Prescriptive knowledge, by contrast, prescribes how things should be to attain a desired end." They "denote varieties of explicit knowledge. To these we must add [...] tacit knowledge [...]. Tacit knowledge and prescriptive knowledge are closely related in practice in that they have to do with procedures. They can thus both be described as procedural knowledgeprocedural [...]" [58].

Knowledge growth in engineering provides an epistemic account of techno-logical innovation [58]. One potential source of emerging technological risk is *uncertainty* in *engineering design knowledge* with respect to technical as well as environmental factors (e.g. social organisations, communities of practice, evolving operational profiles, increasing performance requirements). This can take a mani-fest form when there is a clear deficiency in explicit knowledge either because it is impossible to obtain some knowledge at a particular time (e.g. due to some issue in determining a specification) or because some aspect has been overlooked (e.g. some vulnerability in a component goes undiscovered). Uncertainty in procedural knowledge is more likely to lead to incompatibilities due to different interpretations of identically described procedures or to gaps or inconsistencies in procedures.

Knowledge uncertainty provides useful insights and a partial account of sources of emerging technological risk [22]. It is necessary to adopt design processes that help select design solutions that are likely to function in future (foreseen) opera-tional conditions taking into account how uncertainty in engineering design knowl-edge introduces risk into these processes. Evolutionary design processes attempt to address knowledge growth, uncertainty and three main underlying *evolutionary drivers* (or, *drivers of technology evolution*): *functional failure*, *presumptive anomaly* and the need to *reduce uncertainty* in design knowledge [58] by flexibly incorpo-rating new explicit and procedural knowledge that becomes available during the whole engineering process.

Viewed from a knowledge growth perspective we can see how the need to incor-porate new knowledge into the engineering process drives different methodologies, which deal with different kinds of mistakes or errors (e.g. not understanding the environment, faulty process, faulty execution of process). Functional failures are characteristics of increasing performance requirements under unforeseen operational conditions. *Failures*, or *errors*, provide a source of engineering knowledge [50, 51], although design faults also represent a threat to system dependability [8, 11]. The evolutionary process of searching from knowledge and designing innovations is supported by the analysis of past design errors. *Errors*, or *faults* [8, 11], in design represent a rich source of engineering knowledge [50, 51]. *Learning by mistakes* is a fundamental paradigm of engineering. Growth in engineering design knowledge is therefore a compound learning process (e.g. *social learning* involves *learning by interacting* or *learning by doing* with respect to technology [61]).

1.3.2 Knowledge Negotiation

Technologies and their associated engineering knowledge incorporate social (e.g. organisational) interactions into structured designs. For example, the *system approach* focuses on how heterogeneous artefacts form and are accumulated to form technolo-gies that are incorporated into systems [32]. The engineering knowledge perspective stresses how technological artefacts emerge as result of design activities. Design activities give rise to *technology trajectories*, or the apparently "normal" *evolution of technology*, consisting of "subsequent" *technical changes* [43, 44] that derive from the design process. In contrast, sociological accounts of engineering knowledge highlight the *Social Shaping of Technology* (SST) where design processes are not awarded a privileged position in the social processes surrounding the development and diffusion of technologies and products.

The SST explores diverse social processes that shape the emergence of technologies and their diffusion and deployment in products and systems [42, 60]. From an SST perspective, social accounts of the development and diffusion of technologies include processes of invention, innovation and design and there is no need to give priority to any particular group of processes.

The SST perspective emphasises the notion of *heterogeneous engineering*[5] as (design) solutions in search of problems, rather than problems to be solved or problems in search of solutions [43, 44]. Separating knowledge from technology is just an artificial segmentation for representing cycles of discoveries and innovations. Innovation cycles involve technological evolution with respect to *engineering knowledge*, *technology* and *communities of practice*. Communities of practice shape technology innovation by selecting, adopting, adapting and evolving available technology and knowledge and the communities co-evolve through this process. If we ignore the role of the various communities of practice that cluster round technologies and knowledge about the technologies then we neglect important factors affecting the development, adoption and implementation of technologies and the risks associated with these processes. If we restrict our view of discovery and innovation to the classical deterministic engineering perspective then we risk the controversial *paradox of proving the correctness of technology* [40]. SST provides important tools to investigate the risks associated with the complex relationships between technologies and communities of practice.

In summary, the perspective of the SST emphasises the role of social processes and so takes account of many aspects of risk that are neglected if we focus on technology. For example, risk perception of technology evolution is often neglected but it can play a key role in shaping approaches to risk mitigation. For example, technology evolution is often highly disruptive to work practice and so taking the perception

---

[5] This is in accordance with the SST theory [42, 60], which argues that technology innovation arises from *heterogeneous engineering* that shapes socio-technical systems. The essays collected in [32] give an historical account of the *Systems Approach*: "practitioners and proponents embrace a holistic vision. They focus on the interconnections among subsystems and components, taking special note of the interfaces between components. What is significant is that system builders include heterogeneous components, such as mechanical, electrical, and organisational parts, in a single system. Organisational parts might be managerial structures, such as a military command, or political entities, such as a government bureau. Organisational components not only interact with technical ones but often reflect their characteristics. For instance, a management organisation for presiding over the development of an intercontinental missile system might be divided into divisions that mirror the parts of the missile being designed." A socio-historical account of the technological innovation of missile guidance systems highlights how engineering knowledge is the result of social activities shaping technology that involve heterogeneous engineering not just of technical artefacts but also people, organisations, cultures... [43]: "people had to be engineered, too—persuaded to suspend their doubts, induced to provide resources, trained and motivated to play their parts in a production process unprecedented in its demands. Successfully inventing the technology turned out to be heterogeneous engineering, the engineering of the social as well as the physical world."

of relevant communities of practice helps uncover risk that would otherwise remain undiscovered. In considering technology evolution the synergy between the social shaping and technology trajectory approach can be considerable because it is possible technology trajectories give us some account of design decisions with respect to technology evolution while the social shaping approach helps contextualise with respect to communities of practice.

1.3.3 Knowledge Granularity

Organisations often advocate technology innovation as a means of improving performance (e.g. increased safety). Unfortunately, uncontrolled and misunderstood introduction of new technology can have unexpected and unpredictable effects [49]. There are many drivers for innovation, e.g. including cost, efficiency arguments, obsolescence. Constant has also introduced the notions of "presumptive and functional-failure anomalies" that characterise future operational conditions or requirements and emphasise potential limitations of current systems thereby increasing uncertainty in the operation of the system [18]:

> presumptive anomaly which depends solely on a relationship between technological practice and scientific theory, and anomalies of the functional-failure type, which include failure to work, technological disequilibrium, and the systemic phenomenon described as technological co-evolution.

Design processes seek to reduce uncertainty by specific activities (e.g. system testing, code analysis, simulations). The engineering knowledge perspective emphasises that creating knowledge and reducing uncertainty are community activities depending on work practices and (social) interactions. Thus, from an organisational viewpoint, "information difficulties" represent "barriers to organisational learning" that often results in increased risk perception or more diffuse concerns arising from perceived difficulties around the management of the technology. The "man-made disasters model" stresses that information difficulties as barriers inhibit organisational learning [52] . It identifies four types of information difficulties: (1) latent or misunderstood critical errors or events, (2) dangerous preconditions in ill-structured and constantly changing situations, (3) uncertainty and (4) minimisation of danger despite emerging information or signals working. These issues often cluster around the *safety culture* within the organisation (e.g. see [30, 31] for a review of relevant work on safety culture). Tackling issues in organisational learning requires the integration of different approaches and perspectives that balance technical approaches to risk with attempts to take account of social processes that shape technology risk (e.g. see [9] for an example of socio-technical approach tailored for a specific domain or organisation).

Central to the growth of engineering knowledge is the role of communities of practice that highlight the epistemic nature of engineering knowledge. Their activities and interactions are major drivers for the creation of engineering knowledge that enables technology innovation.[6] Empirical analyses of work practices (e.g. see [1, 2]) highlight how organisational knowledge and technology innovation interact deeply to shape the way innovations diffuse throughout organisations and how the technology is shaped and evolved through that process of diffusion [19–21].

A strong theme in social studies of technological innovation is the tension between local—*micro*—and global—*macro*—knowledge. In particular, this work explores issues around de-contextualising local knowledge to create knowledge that can be communicated globally and processes of recontextualisation where attempts are made to relocate global knowledge in a local context. Industrial case studies drawn from the industrial manufacturing domain highlight how software artefacts incorporate organisational knowledge [19]. The *transfer of knowledge* into software artefacts involves processes of generalisation and contextualisation. These processes can enable coordination and communication between different organisational units, or communities of practice (e.g. engineers and designers) if shifts of context are well managed. Embedding organisational knowledge into software artefacts involves a co-evolutionary process. The embedding process consists of knowledge acquisition and generalisation for codification and simplification, whereas knowledge utilisation requires reinstatement of subjectivity and local knowledge.

Although it is impossible to draw a distinction between the local and the global levels abstractly, the distinction is usually clear in any particular context. In analysing organisational knowledge it is often valuable to consider different levels of granularity—e.g. at the micro level, where individuals use technology artefacts enabling organisational memory to be (re)used, or at the macro level, where groups of people (or communities of practice) shape technology artefacts enabling organisational knowledge to be shared. Global contexts are those in which knowledge cannot be re-contextualised quickly (or at all), because there are no mechanisms to achieve this but this de-contextualised knowledge can be useful, for example in identifying trends across many locations. Local contexts are those in which knowledge can be re-contextualised when necessary (often by informal means) and this can be critical in ensuring the robustness and resilience of systems.

Organisational (memory) knowledge involves both the (technology) artefacts storing knowledge and the processes enabling knowledge management and reuse [1, 2]. Taking into account a social perspective of technology allows us to investigate how organisations 'transfer' knowledge into technology innovation [20]. This is in accordance with the SST perspective which emphasises that technology innovation arises from a process of heterogeneous engineering that shapes both the social and technical elements of systems and their interactions. Failing to understands the

---

[6] Engineering activities contribute towards knowledge and technology innovation, which results from interactions between communities of practice, which "[...] supply a number of functions essential to the learning process." *Competition* [...] and *cooperation* emerge as processes "to tackle difficult practical problems [...]" and to [...] "support and aid in overcoming difficulties" [58].

underlying mechanisms and their social perspectives exposes organisations to socio-technical hazards. These can result in many different forms of undependability, e.g. technology failures, mispractices ('human errors'), misinterpretation of information across communities of practice or reduced services.

1.4 Human Dimensions of Technology Risk

Technology-focused accounts of risk face various difficulties in uncovering complex failure mechanisms. A narrow viewpoint of analysis focusing on technical aspects can be misleading and erroneous in classifying "system failures" due to "human error" [28, 34]. At the microscopic level, "human errors" in technology interaction (e.g. human–machine interaction) concern interaction issues, which highlight subtle contingencies between, for example, human performance and (system) reliability. Understanding system failure modes allows users, or human operators, to develop *trust* in technology, *confidence* in (their) work practices and knowledge of the system. Social accounts of trust (e.g. see [16, 24, 25] for an account of trust) and risk perception [22, 55] stress the interaction between trust, risk and knowledge. A social viewpoint provides a balanced intersection of risk, trust and technology considerations that takes account of the positive aspects of error as a means of gaining knowledge and trust in complex systems.

The different relationships (e.g. independence, mediation and moderation) between trust and risk emphasise different emergent behaviours of socio-technical systems. The characterisation of trust and risk suggests that the underlying constructs interact in the formation of trust and the perception of risk. This interaction originates in social aspects of trust and risk. The interaction between trust and risk perception provides the basis for an analysis of social aspects of technology. For instance, the interaction between trust and risk perception gives rise to the phenomenon of *risk homeostasis*—the result of overtrusting technology—consisting in a reduction of risk perception due to advances in technology [28]. The level of risk perception is constant, although increasing demands on performance push the system to work close to hazardous conditions.[7] Furthermore, the growing complexity of technology and the tight coupling of technology affect risk perception and expose human perfor-

---

[7] The phenomenon of risk homeostasis affects many types of system. For instance, the anti-lock braking system (ABS) of a car can induce drivers to accept increasing technology risk because as drivers experience ABS they come to trust in its performance and this allows them to drive in a way that would be seen as too risky in a non-ABS car but the drivers are unaware of all the performance characteristics of the ABS system and so could be exposing themselves to excessive risk [28]. Other domains, such as air traffic control (ATC) and Avionics, involve "complex systems" facing risk homeostasis [49]: "there are some unique structural conditions in this industry that promote safety, and despite complexity and coupling, technological fixes can work in some areas. Yet we continue to have accidents because aircraft and the airways still remain somewhat complex and tightly coupled, but also because those in charge continue to push the system to its limits. Fortunately, the technology and skilled pilots and air traffic controllers remain a bit ahead of the pressures, and the result has been that safety has continued to increase, though not as markedly as in early decades".

mance to system failures [49]. The problem is then two-fold. The first concern is with the complexity management of systems. The second is with the coupling management of these complex systems. This is the case, for instance, in software development for some classes of system. However, many of the more successful large-scale systems consist of potentially quite complex components that are socially managed in a lightweight manner and have relatively low coupling. Many embedded systems do meet the complexity/coupling criteria, because they have a high-complexity management and have tight coupling—e.g. modern automotive systems—but as these become socialised and black-boxed the complexity management diminishes.

An effective *Human Reliability Analysis* (HRA) requires an understanding of *human cognition* [28], that is, it is necessary to understand and analyse those cognitive processes characterising human behaviour. *Distributed Cognition* theory highlights how distributed artefacts enable human cognition as a negotiated process within communities of practice [17, 27, 48]. *Bounded rationality* is another aspect of human cognition [26]. It provides an alternative perspective to probabilistic approaches of knowledge. Reasoning and decision-making processes often rely on limited information and constrained environmental conditions. Understanding bounded rationality allows us the identification of fast and frugal heuristics, which provide a characterisation of human reasoning and decision-making in real situations exhibiting limited computational capacities and resources. The analysis in situated cases identifies in fast and frugal heuristics valuable tools for understanding the processes of reasoning and decision-making under constrained knowledge. The performance of fast and frugal heuristics exhibits some sensitivity to information structure (or information ecology), that is, how information is distributed or organised in the environment. Therefore, at the microscopic level, cognition involves processes and artefacts characterising technology interaction. At the macroscopic level, cognition involves negotiation (within emerging social networks) [46]. To what extent negotiation takes place depends on group socialities [22]. Different types of individuals or groups (e.g. "individualists", "egalitarians", "hierarchists" and "fatalists" [22, 29]) have different dispositions to act in a particular way (in, say, how they recognise and mitigate dangers) that arise from their Grid/Group positions (that is, their positions within the group with respect to its size and structure) and rules. This, again, stresses the SST. Moreover, a lack of understanding of the different hierarchical layers and granularity of interaction can result in failure to recognise important risks in systems thereby exposing organisations to these emerging technological risks [53].

1.5 Risk Society

The traditional view is that technological systems have flaws, hence, on the basis of the frequency of manifestation and severity of the consequences, risk assessment drives the management of flaws. Risk in technology, unfortunately, is more heterogeneous, difficult and complex to capture, because technology is deeply embedded in social and organisational contexts. This complicates the analysis of risk associated with socio-technical systems. The *Risk Society* provides a social account of risk [12]. Although the risk society provides only a partial account of risk [39, 45], it analyses an important shift in modern society from the social production of wealth to the social production of risk [3]. Analysing the distribution problems and conflicts arising emphasises the nature of techno-scientifically produced risks. The risk society is, therefore, concerned with trade-offs involved in the systematic production of risks and hazards as part of *modernisation* [35], often involving technology innovation.

> The theory of *re-modernisation* advocates the existence of diverse modernities [35]. The analysis of re-modernisation draws a comparison between the *Actor-Network Theory* (ANT) and the *risk society*. The work in [35] rejects the term "modern" as often advocated by technologists. It argues that, on the contrary, we "have never been modern". It analyses features (e.g. reflexive behaviours, externalities) of "modern" societies with respect to the similarities and differences between actor-network and risk theories. It argues that although re-modernisation may or may not be ongoing the cases for or against are not particularly strong. Finally, it points out similarities and differences between the ANT and the risk society.

A key feature in the risk of the analysis of the risk society is the move from seeing danger and risk as something inherent in the world (e.g. earthquakes, flooding, hurricanes) to something that is associated with human activity (e.g. the risks of nuclear power, genetic engineering). Thus risks produced as part of modernisation and so require management processes to handle these risks associated with modern production. The aim (of risk assessment, management and mitigation) is to minimise, prevent and mitigate arising risks or "latent side effects" of modernisation. The production and trade of hazards characterise the risk society. In that regard, the *Information Society* (IS) is a particular instance of the risk society. An emergent market in the "modern" IS is the one that exploits *security vulnerabilities* [4–7]. The risk society captures and explains the economics of vulnerabilities. For many modern technologies the costs of managing associated risks can become a major determinant of their success and entire business sectors can be built on the mitigation of certain classes of risk, for example the businesses built on the mitigation of PC security risks.

An important characteristic of modernisation is its "reflexivity" [13, 35] where considerable effort is devoted to consider the process of modernisation. Unfortunately, the reflexivity of modernisation has both positive and negative effects and this reflexive activity opens up a vista of new vulnerabilities for the risk society itself. Modern economics is a particularly fruitful source of examples of the effects of reflexivity within economic activity—both the development of economic theory and the 'real' economy. Modern economics in our society powerfully exhibits some distinguishing features of the risk society [41]. "Performativity" in modern economics is one of the leading exemplars of the general phenomenon of reflexivity in the risk society. Hence, economics and technology are important interacting facets of the risk society that work together to amplify their effects. They are key elements in our risk distributing society (rather than a wealth distributing society).

The process of distributing risk is not economically neutral, the process of risk distribution generates considerable economic activity. In our modern society the scale of risk is global and huge resource is devoted to the process of distributing and managing risk.[8] For our purposes the notion of performativity is interesting because it introduces a regress of reflection on the economy, models of the economy, models of models, etc. that are essentially reflections on risk and the match, or lack of match between model and activity introduces many new potential risks.

Economics is a highly reflexive activity because part of economics is to create theories and models of human activity that incorporate the model or theory-creating activity. Performativity is the process whereby the creation of models or theories affects 'real' economic activity. A possible (hierarchical) classification of the performativity of economics consists of [41]: "generic" *performativity*, "effective" *performativity*, "Barnesian" *performativity* and *counter-performativity*.

- "Generic" perfomativity: "an aspect of economics (a theory, model, concept, procedure, data set, etc.) is used by participants in economic processes, regulators, etc."
- "Effective" performativity: "the practical use of an aspect of economics has an effect on economic processes."
- "Barnesian" performativity: "practical use of an aspect of economics makes economic processes more like their depiction by economics."
- Counter performativity: "practical use of an aspect of economics makes economic processes less like their depiction by economics."

Our modern society depends on technology. The question then is: *where is the risk in technology innovation?* It is possible to distinguish different types of risks (e.g. "perceived through science", "perceived directly" and "virtual risk" [29]), which require different types of risk management.[9] In particular, technology risk analysis provides input to the class of risk perceived through science. The way people perceive

---

[8] Collateralised Debt Obligations (CDOs) are a good example of products that package and offer complex means to manage financial risk. CDOs are new technologies with new risks. Many experts, i.e. bankers and hedge fund operators, had little access to risk information, despite the risks being accessible to them in terms of exposure.

[9] Even early in the industrial age risk was seen as an important element in the acceptance of technologies. Thomas Edison opposed the introduction of Alternating Current (AC) electricity

and behave with respect to the arising technology risk that makes technology society more of a risk society. However, often debating about risk without a clear 'definitive' position gives rise to virtual risk. The concept of risk is directly influenced by the concept of *reflexive modernisation* [12].

Potential or actual accidents are interpreted and prioritised according to the interests of the interpreting group or society. That is, it is important to understand how people position themselves with respect to (technology) risk in the risk society. The position with respect to risk crosses organisational boundaries, classes and divisions of labour. *Cultural Theory* (CT), introduced by Mary Douglas, provides a very high-level analysis of how different groups are predisposed to interpret risk [22]. This is based on two dimensions she identifies that help to place social groups within the broader culture. *Group* is a measure of how much external regulation is exerted on a group, whereas *Grid* is a measure of the strength of internal group regulation [22]:

> Group means the outside boundary that people have erected between themselves and the outside world. Grid means all the other social distinctions and delegations of authority that they use to limit how people behave to one another.

Analysis of risk perception at this very abstract level would say the High Grid + Low Group cultures would take a fatalistic view of dangers considering most phenomena to be out of their control and so effectively random. In contrast, Low Group + Low Grid cultures exhibit "individualism" where there is no need for regulation and control and risks can be resolved through individual negotiation (e.g. argue that *Global Warming* is not a risk but an opportunity for the right person) [22]. High Grid + High Group cultures exhibit "hierarchy" and respond to risk in a bureaucratic way, attempting to regulate and standardise (e.g. global warming should be tackled by changes in building codes, traffic legislation, industrial law, etc. to ensure carbon reduction targets are achieved). Any sufficiently complex organisation will comprise a rich mixture of differently constituted communities of practice and their sensitivity and response to risks will differ. This combined with expertise and ability to bring about change will differ significantly from risk to risk so organisational response to risk is a complex matter. Knowledge distribution creates awareness of risk. Knowledge is embedded in distributed resources. The ability to access such knowledge is related to expertise and power—e.g. a probabilistic risk assessment may be available transparently but it is likely that only a few who know about statistics will have good access to that knowledge.

The more accessible resources are, the more likely people are to acquire knowledge about risk. However, their response to specific risks will depend on the perspective of the various groups they belong to and their power within the organisations they work for. Similar variability of response to risks arises in the analysis of technology complexity [49]—typical questions are: *how does technology complexity relates to its risk? What are the social implications (with respect to risk) of technology?* On the one hand, considering, for instance, technology, environment and management, it is quite

---

(Footnote 9 Continued)
supplies and felons executed by the electric chair were said to have been "Westinghoused" to emphasise the claimed risks of the AC system being promoted by George Westinghouse [14].

possible for quite senior managers to argue that very highly complex technologies are fairly easy to manage (e.g. the phone network is complex yet involves relatively low management complexity because traditional phone systems have *black-boxed* many of the management issues—but this is changing because companies are looking at much more complex management strategies for mobile networks to squeeze more performance out of the network). On the other hand, despite the use of technology barrier mechanisms that enable us to identify 'acceptable values' of risk (on which concepts like ALARP are developed[10]), the reflexive nature of the risk society opens up the possibility of gaming organisational models to identify potential, as yet unrealised, risks (e.g. "Swiss cheese model") of defences [12, 53].

Knowledge (hence, technology) acquires a different role enabling political and social debates in the risk society. Knowledge about risk consists of projections of dangers (or hazards) to the future. For instance, the Y2K (Year 2000) hazard concentrated the attention of people on potential risks of technology systems [49]. Unfortunately risk involves uncertainty in knowledge. Therefore, uncertainty exposes the limitations of the *calculability of risk* [40]. That is, the calculability of risk is a socio-technical problem, rather than a purely technical one. Uncertainty characterises the risk society. Moreover, the risk society exhibits particular features. First, modernisation involves new types of risks. Second social structures (or positions) expose people to risk differently. Risk exposure crosses the classical organisational boundaries or divisions of labour. Due to the reflexive nature of the risk society, identifying trade-offs and negotiating knowledge involve strategies and policies giving rise to social as well as political debates (or decision-making games). Knowledge about risk therefore acquires a critical social and political power, because it enables and positions (that is, empowers) people with respect to risk. Finally, hazards and risks (or consequential catastrophes) have the potential to influence risk perception. Moreover, risk perception is subject to the phenomenon of social-amplification of risk [55]. Therefore, it is mandatory to include both social and cultural aspects in the formulation of technology risk. That is, it is unrealistic to characterise technology risk without including emerging social structures and mechanisms.

The *Cultural Theory* of risk demonstrates how different constitutions of social groupings within an organisation behave with respect to hazards [22]. The concepts of safety culture or safety climate identify and describe "shared corporate values within an organisation which influences the attitudes and behaviours of its members" [31]. Safety culture highlights how different organisational or social structures, that is, groups select, hence perceive, risk [22]. For instance, a *safety culture* arises in a High Grid + High Group setting, because there is high internal cohesion and stringent demands on accountability to external authorities so a particular regime involving audit and transparency evolves. This situation is present to a certain extent in the organisational structures and relationships between Air Navigation Service

---

[10] The *quantification* of risk supports decision-making processes for the acceptance of a particular risk. Decision acceptance depends on whether or not a particular level of risk is *As Low As Reasonably Possible* (ALARP). A measurable risk that complies with the ALARP principle is considered a "tolerable risk" from an engineering viewpoint [57].

Providers (ANSPs) and Civil Aviation Authorities. In contrast, the *safety culture* in healthcare (in terms of organisational structures and relationships) where we see a Low Grid + High Group culture takes a "collectivist" stance. As a consequence healthcare is less transparent and is only made accountable in extreme cases via the law. This characterisation of risk perception, with respect to social structures, highlights a correlation between social structures and risk (perception), hence the presence of subcultures.[11] For instance, highly structured and regulated groups perceive risk differently than unorganised groups, who feel a lack of control over risk selection. The *Psychometric Paradigm* of risk perception highlights similar results [55]. In contrast to Cultural Theory, it advocates a quantitative and qualitative framework for studying risk perception.[12] An increase in risk perception is twofold. On the one hand, risk may have increased. On the other hand, our knowledge of risk may have increased. Risks can therefore relate to knowledge and because risks are often unrealised in the sense they refer to an as yet inexperienced future the catalogue of risks for any technological system is also a catalogue of the focus and concerns of a wide range of groups engaged in the implementation of a project.

Much of this broad socio-technical analysis of risk casts light on risk in organisations. The analysis of potential risks in organisations requires us to understand and focus on how the dominance of particular groups de-emphasises certain classes of risk. For example, in security standards one might expect to see High Grid + High Group cultures (exhibiting hierarchical-collective controls) dominating standards formation. This might suggests standards would arise that emphasise the role of deviants as a source of risks. This is very evident in security risk assessment guidelines (e.g. [56]), which emphasise deviants and tend to neglect internal threats due to excessive diligence of some groups (e.g. system administrators in applying the latest patches that might deny a legitimate user access to some service). Similar aspects emerge in the study of the economics of information security in which emerging network topology and behaviour (e.g. "strategy-proof") affect security aspects [5].

Further understanding these types of mechanisms in the design of technology innovation allows the identification of organisational risks that might otherwise be overlooked. Organisations comprise many different groups, whose risk perception may differ radically and whose need for, and attitude to, system change also varies depending on role and environment. Since different participants in an organisation potentially have very different perception of the existence and severity of risks,

---

[11]   This correlation manifests in the presence of subcultures [31]: Subcultures are likely to develop when employees within the same organisation experience different working conditions. Work groups within an organisation are likely to view risk differently depending on the type of work they do. In general, subcultures are not seen as undesirable and it can be argued that they provide useful contextual insight into the different risk and hazards experienced by workgroups."

[12]   The *psychometric paradigm* of risk perception provides a "theoretical framework that assumes risk is subjectively defined by individuals who may be influenced by a wide array of psychological, social, institutional and cultural factors" [55]. The underlying assumption is that "with appropriate design of survey instruments, many of these factors and their interrelationships can be quantified and modelled in order to illuminate the responses of individuals and their societies to the hazards that confront them" [55].

it is necessary to consider issues of risk perception to help manage risk in complex organisations. It is important to highlight how socialities explain, understand and perceive risk, in particular, with respect to technology innovation. This requires us to develop mechanisms for handling risk arising for ongoing processes of change in organisational systems, that is, how to manage the risks associated with changes in complex technologies [15].

1.6 Interdisciplinary Technological Risk

The study of *technology risk* involves the analysis of how technology exposes society to different threats or hazards. The *risk society* is concerned with how technological hazards affect different groups [12, 22]. Risk complexity manifests in how technology hazards propagate across organisational or social boundaries (e.g. division of labour, social classes) [22, 49]. Knowledge about technology informs debates, empowers social groups and allows them to position themselves with respect to technology risk [12]. Various studies—e.g. [12, 22, 47, 49]—investigate and define a broad spectrum of socio-technical accounts of technology risk. These range from a *microscopic* (e.g. how individuals behave with respect to technology and perceive risk) to a *macroscopic* (e.g. organisational, social, socio-political, environmental) analysis of technology risk.

Classifications of risk studies highlight how different accounts of risk lead to different understandings of socio-technical problems [36, 37]. The combination of different levels of investigations—e.g. "micro/meso/macro"—together with diverse types of models and approaches—e.g. "normative (or prescriptive)" as opposed to "descriptive"—allows a characterisation of different risk problems.[13] On the one hand, the interpretation of "complex causalities" that characterise "complex interactions" [23, 49] triggering 'unpredictable' failures[14] (or failure modes). On the other hand, the epistemology of the investigations of failures draws backward the

---

[13]   The problem is then to establish or interpret a link between different levels of analysis [37]: "it must be acknowledged however that no conflicting view is implied here between human factors (a micro level) and organisational factors (a meso–macro level) as it is believed that by principle links do exist between the two approaches. The difficulty is however a well known interdisciplinary and scientific difficulty where individual levels with for example psychological and psycho-cognitive insights and a higher level with sociological, psycho-sociological or anthropological dimensions need conceptual and empirical articulations." Diverse approaches and methodologies pinpoint different risk accounts and identify different practices of investigating technology risk [37]: "These two positions—descriptive and normative—help defining a continuum along which different investigation processes (implying different type of rationales, resources, models, time and access of information but also purposes and method) can be unfolded, depending on the context of the accident, its scope but also on the resources and competence of the people in charge of applying the tools and methodologies."

[14]   Complex causalities characterise the social dimensions of technology [37]: "Complexity [...] provides a picture of the human and social world where causalities are not linear, where their effects can be by nature unpredictable and counter intuitive. The nature of this unpredictability is found in the high number of interrelated, self-organised entities that are always affected by changes

causalities leading to accidents [37]. These dimensions, i.e. micro/meso/macro and normative/descriptive, identify a framework for the classification of the modelling approaches underlying the investigations of past accidents [37]. Similarly, it is possible to identify different organisational levels, from "closed system models" to "open system models" [36], for the classification of safety approaches and the underlying models with respect to different social levels of analysis. These classifications position research and investigation methodologies according to *topologies of socialities* (e.g. micro/meso/macro) and *system boundaries* (e.g. closed as opposed to open system models) [36, 37].

Disciplinary boundaries between accounts inhibit and narrow the scope of analysis of technology risk. Unfortunately, this often limits our understanding of technology risk and its underlying mechanisms as a whole. At its simplest, there is a disconnect between different levels of granularities. Drawing similarities and links between diverse accounts of risk supports cross-fertilisation between scientific and practitioner communities, who seek to understand risk in technology innovation. Unveiling contingencies between the social and the technical enhances our understanding of where socio-technical risks reside. An interdisciplinary account of *emerging technological risk* seeks to establish links between technical and social accounts of technology risk. But social accounts of risk can be very different—e.g. the economic account begins with the *individual*, whereas the sociological one begins with the *group*, contrasting a *market* view of risk with a *cultural* view of risk.

This book discusses the links between technical and social accounts of technology risk in terms of complex *socio-technical hazards*. In order to establish such links, the focus is on the following questions:

1. *How does technology cross organisational (e.g. social and cultural) boundaries and expose organisations to risk across their boundaries?* Understanding the mechanisms underlying how technology supports diverse forms of social organisations allows us to address the risk associated with *unbounded* technology.
2. *How does technology innovation capture evolutionary processes?* Social interaction shapes technology. In order to understand the contingencies between technology innovation and evolutionary processes (characterised by social interaction), it is necessary to unveil how technology innovation affects work practice.
3. *How do communities gather together around technology?* It is necessary to understand how communities of practice affect technology development. Accidentally, technology innovation exposes communities of practices to reduced diversity and increased common vulnerability. Hence, it exposes communities

---

(Footnote 14 Continued)
in the system, through interactions and feedbacks, and thus leading to unexpected and emergent patterns. Circular causalities [...] are a more suitable approach than a linear one when it comes to thinking of causalities in the social and human world, and therefore in organisations. These evolutions are not fully predictable, and the future is consequently hardly deterministic when it comes to organisations."

of practice to complex system failures (or complex causalities). Understanding the contingencies between the social and the technical requires us to investigate mechanisms of failure propagation across organisational boundaries.

This book draws on accounts of risk that contribute towards an interdisciplinary understanding of *emerging technological risk*. It points out work that falls into the different scales, i.e. microscopic and macroscopic. The potential benefit is an interdisciplinary study that links these two scales of analysis. A review of relevant work outlines and emphasises how multidisciplinary work characterises the relationship between scales of analysis. It also assesses the promise of new tools and techniques that arise from interdisciplinary work on emergent risk in socio-technical systems. This book articulates emerging technological risk in terms of three classes of socio-technical hazards, namely, *Boundary Hazards*, *Evolutionary Hazards* and *Performativity Hazards*. It explores these classes of socio-technical hazards, which arise from the interdisciplinary study of technological risk. These classes of socio-technical hazards support risk analysis from microscopic to macroscopic scale and vice versa. Hence, they provide an account of technology risk as a whole. They look at how diverse risk perspectives affect each other. In order to address the above point, it is necessary to develop an account of emerging technological risk, which understands diverse perspectives of technological risk. This, moreover, contributes to ease conflicting views of multidisciplinary accounts of risk into an interdisciplinary discussion of *emerging technological risk*. This process underpins the risk of technology innovation.

References

1. Ackerman MS, Halverson CA (2000) Reexamining organizational memory. Commun ACM 43(1):59–64. doi:10.1145/323830.323845
2. Ackerman MS, Halverson CA (2004) Organizational memory as objects processes and trajectories: an examination of organizational memory in use. Comput Support Coop Work 13(2):155–189. doi:10.1023/B:COSU.0000045805.77534.2a
3. Adam B, Beck U, Van Loon J (eds) (2000) The risk society and beyond: critical issues for social theory. SAGE Publications, London
4. Anderson R (2001) Why information security is hard—an economic perspective. In: Proceedings of the 17th annual computer security applications conference, ACSAC 2001. IEEE Computer Society, New York, pp 358–365. doi:10.1109/ACSAC.2001.991552
5. Anderson R, Moore T (2006) The economics of information security. Science 314(5799):610–613. doi:10.1126/science.1130992
6. Anderson R, Moore T (2007) The economics of information security: a survey and open questions. In: Proceedings of the fourth bi-annual conference on the economics of the software and internet industries
7. Anderson RJ (2008) Security engineering: a guide to building dependable distributed systems, 2nd edn. Wiley, New York
8. Arlat J, Blanquart J-P, Costes A, Crouzet Y, Deswarte Y, Fabre J-C, Guillermain H, Kaâniche M, Kanoun K, Laprie J-C, Mazet C, Powell D, Rabéjac C, Thévenod P (1998) Dependability Handbook. Technical Report 98–346, LAAS

9. Atkinson C, Eldabi T, Paul RJ, Pouloudi A (2001) Investigating integrated socio-technical approaches to health informatics. In: Proceedings of the 34th Hawaii international conference on system sciences. IEEE Computer Society, pp 1–10. doi:10.1109/HICSS.2001.926578

10. Aven T, Kristensen V (2005) Perspectives on risk: review and discussion of the basis for establishing a unified and holistic approach. Reliab Eng Syst Saf 90(1):1–14. doi:10.1016/j.ress.2004.10.008

11. Avižienis A, Laprie J-C, Randell B, Landwehr C (2004) Basic concepts and taxonomy of dependable and secure computing. IEEE Trans Depend Secure Comput 1(1):11–33. doi:10.1109/TDSC.2004.2

12. Beck U (1992) Risk society: towards a new modernity. SAGE Publications, London

13. Beck U, Bonss W, Lau C (2003) The theory of reflexive modernization: problematic hypotheses and research programme. Theory Cult Soc 20(2):1–33. doi:10.1177/0263276403020002001

14. Bernstein T (1973) A grand success. IEEE Spectr 10(2):54–58. doi:10.1109/MSPEC. 1973.5216688

15. Borodzicz EP (2005) Risk, crisis and security management. Wiley, Chichester

16. Bottitta S, Felici M (2006) Understanding and learning trust: a review, characterization and tool. In: Guedes Soares C, Zio E (eds) Safety and reliability for managing risk, proceedings of the European safety and reliability conference 2006, ESREL 2006, vol 2. Taylor and Francis, pp 1273–1280

17. Bowker GC, Star SL (1999) Sorting things out: classification and its consequences. The MIT Press, Cambridge

18. Constant EW II (1984) Communities and hierarchies: structure in the practice of science and technology. In: Laudan R (ed) The Nature of technological knowledge: are models of scientific change relevant? Kluwer, Dordrecht

19. D'Adderio L (2001) Crafting the virtual prototype: how firms integrate knowledge and capabilities across organisational boundaries. Res Policy 30(9):1409–1424. doi:10.1016/S0048-7333(01)00159-7

20. D'Adderio L (2003) Configuring software, reconfiguring memories: the influence of integrated systems on the reproduction of knowledge and routines. Ind Corp Chang 12(2):321–350

21. D'Adderio L (2003) Inside the virtual product: how organisations create knowledge through software. Edward Elgar, Cheltenham

22. Douglas M, Wildavsky A (1982) Risk and culture: an essay on the selection of technological and environmental dangers. University of California Press, Berkeley

23. Felici M (2006) Capturing emerging complex interactions: safety analysis in air traffic management. Reliab Eng Syst Saf 91(12):1482–1493. doi:10.1016/j.ress.2006.01.010

24. Felici M (2006) Trust strategies: motivations from the air traffic management domain. In: Guedes Soares C, Zio E (eds) Safety and reliability for managing risk, proceedings of the european safety and reliability conference 2006, ESREL 2006, vol 3. Taylor and Francis, pp 1797–1804

25. Felici M (2007) Trust strategies and policies in complex socio-technical safety-critical domains: an analysis of the air traffic management domain. In: Guelfi N, Buchs D (eds) Proceedings of the 3rd international workshop on rapid integration of software engineering techniques, RISE 2006, LNCS, vol 4401. Springer, Heidelberg, pp 51–65. doi: 10.1007/978-3-540-71876-5_4

26. Gigerenzer G, Todd PM, The ABC Research Group (1999) Simple heuristics that make us smart. Oxford University Press, New York

27. Halverson CA (2002) Activity theory and distributed cognition: or what does cscw need to do with theories? Comput Support Coop Work 11(1–2):243–267. doi:10.1023/A:1015298005381

28. Hollnagel E (1993) Human reliability analysis: context and control. Academic Press, London

29. HSE (2002) Taking account of societal concerns about risk—framing the problem. Research Report, vol 035, Health and Safety Executive

30. HSE (2005) A review of safety culture and safety climate literature for the development of the safety culture inspection toolkit. Research Report, vol 367, Health and Safety Executive

31. HSL (2002) Safety culture: a review of the literature. Report number HSL/2002/25, Health and Safety Laboratory
32. Hughes, AC, Hughes, TP (eds) (2000) Systems, experts, and computers: the systems approach in management and engineering, world war II and after. The MIT Press, Cambridge
33. IEC (2010) IEC 61508: functional safety of electrical/electronic/programmable electronic safety-related systems. International electrotechnical commission, 2.0 edn
34. Johnson CW (2003) Failure in safety-critical systems: a handbook of accident and incident reporting. University of Glasgow Press, Glasgow
35. Latour B (2003) Is re-modernization occurring—and if so, how to prove it? a commentary on Ulrich Beck. Theory Cult Soc 20(2):35–48. doi:10.1177/0263276403020002002
36. Le Coze J (2005) Are organisations too complex to be integrated in the technical risk assessment and current safety auditing?. Saf Sci 43(8):613–638. doi:10.1016/j.ssci.2005.06.005
37. Le Coze J (2008) Disasters and organisations: from lessons learnt to theorising. Saf Sci 46(1):132–149. doi:10.1016/j.ssci.2006.12.001
38. Leveson NG (1995) Safeware: system safety and computers. Addison-Wesley, Reading
39. Löfstedt, RE, Frewer, L (eds) (1998) The earthscan reader in risk and modern society. Earthscan Publications, London
40. MacKenzie D (2001) Mechanizing proof: computing, risk, and trust. The MIT Press, Cambridge
41. MacKenzie D (2006) An engine, not a camera: how financial models shape markets: inside technology. The MIT Press, Cambridge
42. MacKenzie, D, Wajcman, J (eds) (1999) The social shaping of technology, 2nd edn. Open University Press, Milton Keynes
43. MacKenzie DA (1990) Inventing accuracy: a historical sociology of nuclear missile guidance. The MIT Press, Cambridge
44. MacKenzie DA (1996) Knowing machines: essays on technical change. The MIT Press, Cambridge
45. Mythen G (2004) Ulrich Beck: a critical introduction to the risk society. Pluto Press, London
46. Nardi BA, Whittaker S, Schwarz H (2002) Networkers and their activity in intensional networks. Comput Support Coop Work 11(1–2):205–242. doi:10.1023/A:1015241914483
47. Neumann PG (1995) Computer related risks. The ACM Press, New York
48. Norman DA (1993) Things that make us smart: defining human attributes in the age of the machine. Perseus Books, Reading
49. Perrow C (1999) Normal accidents: living with high-risk technologies. Princeton University Press, New Jersey
50. Petroski H (1982) To engineer is human: the role of failure in successful design. Vintage Books, New York
51. Petroski H (1994) Design paradigms: case histories of error and judgment in engineering. Cambridge University Press, New York
52. Pidgeon N, O'Leary M (2000) Man-made disasters: why technology and organizations (sometimes) fail. Saf Sci 34(1–3):15–30. doi:10.1016/S0925-7535(00)00004-7
53. Reason J (1997) Managing the risks of organizational accidents. Ashgate, Aldershot
54. Rogers Y, Scaife M, Rizzo A (2005) Interdisciplinarity: an emergent or engineered process? In: Derry SJ, Schunn CD, Gernsbacher MA (eds) Interdisciplinary collaboration: an emerging cognitive science. Lawrence Erlbaum Associates, Mahwah
55. Slovic P (2000) The perception of risk. Earthscan Publications, London
56. Stonebumer G, Goguen A, Feringa A (2002) Risk management guide for information technology systems—recommendations of the national institute of standards and technology. NIST, Gaithersburg
57. Storey N (1996) Safety-critical computer systems. Addison-Wesley, Harlow
58. Vincenti WG (1990) What engineers know and how they know it: analytical studies from aeronautical history. The Johns Hopkins University Press, Baltimore

59. Wallace DR, Kuhn DR (1999) Lessons from 342 medical device failures. In: Proceedings of the 4th IEEE International symposium on high-assurance systems engineering, HASE. IEEE Computer Society, pp 123–131

60. Williams R, Edge D (1996) The social shaping of technology. Res Policy 25(6):865–899. doi:10.1016/0048-7333(96)00885-2

61. Williams R, Stewart J, Slack R (2005) Social learning in technological innovation: experimenting with information and communication technologies. Edward Elgar, Cheltenham

Part II
Risk Underpinnings

Chapter 2
Unbounded Technology

Classifications as *Boundary Objects* provide a means for analysing the subtle interactions between communities of practice and technologies. This chapter uses the concept of boundary objects in order to analyse specific hazards, namely, *Boundary Hazards*, which expose organisations to system vulnerabilities. This chapter reviews different case studies. It highlights boundary objects and their mechanisms with respect to communities of practice and technological systems. Lack of understanding of boundary objects and failure to take subtle processes and interaction mechanisms into account in designing and deploying new technology represent potential hazards for technological systems. Technologies expose organisations to hazards across their boundaries. Analysing technological risk then requires an understanding of how hazards spread through organisational boundaries. It is necessary to deal with '*unbounded* technologies. The analysis enhances our ability to understand boundary objects in technological systems and their related risk.

2.1 Classification Systems and Boundary Objects

Classification systems, or simply *classifications*, provide a socio-technical viewpoint in order to analyse technological systems [8]. Classifications, such as information systems or infrastructures, are ubiquitous and pervasive in many professional and application domains. They shape and slice our societies, that is, they provide a means for categorising and gathering information[1] that constitutes *knowledge* in our *modern state* [7] or *risk society* [5]. On the one hand, classifications represent practical tools used in different application domains. On the other hand, classifications capture information flows in systems as well as organisations. For instance, the *International Classification of Diseases* (ICD) emerged as a means for monitoring and analysing diseases and their developments [7, 8, 33].

---

[1] The urge for statistical evidence or knowledge underpins the "modern state" [7] as well as the "risk society" [5], even though they are related accounts of the developments of the modern information society.

S. Anderson and M. Felici, *Emerging Technological Risk*,
DOI: 10.1007/978-1-4471-2143-5_2, © Springer-Verlag London Limited 2012

The *International Classification of Diseases* (ICD), adopted and maintained by the *World Health Organization* (WHO), is part of the *WHO Family of International Classifications*, which provides practical tools for classifying diseases, monitoring their spread over populations, decision making and policy outlining (e.g. identifying contingency measures for isolating diseases) [31,33]. The history of the ICD spans over the last four centuries, from the initial attempts to classify diseases systematically in the eighteenth century to the current tenth revision of the ICD (ICD-10) in the twenty-first century [33]. The first internationally adopted classification was the *International List of Causes of Death*. The changing name over the years captures the shift of the rationale and usage of the classification itself. The history of the ICD highlights a strong relational coupling with the developments of information technologies [7]. The future development of the ICD, i.e. the update to the ICD-11, is driven to some extent by technology too [30, 32]. There is the necessity to address the "information paradox" the patchy and uneven distribution of knowledge that stresses the disparities among countries. The most vulnerable and affected countries are the ones who would benefit most from the implementation of the ICD. Unfortunately, the dividend or lack of technology, as well as financial resources, exacerbates the gaps among countries. Technology innovation plays a critical role in addressing the WHO strategies and supporting its assets. For instance, the concept of e-health is central in the future development of the ICD. The health record intends to link terminologies to classifications in order to enrich the knowledge (i.e. enabling ontology-based terminology systems) and sustain the WHO knowledge network. Moreover, the identification of specific technology, such as the Extensible Markup Language (XML), would drive to some extent future implementation of the ICD and support other functionalities. A practical need is to improve the accessibility and implementation of the ICD by providing, for instance, a *Short Mortality List* (SML) in order to address the information paradox. The history of the ICD shows dependencies between the development of the classification and technology [7]. The better our understanding of their inter-dependencies, the better our ability to design technology systems that rely on classifications.

The classification of *faults*, *errors* and *failures* [4], for instance, enables causal analysis [19] in order to investigate and to assess (system) failures from a system viewpoint [18]. The identification of system vulnerabilities allows us to classify and assess technical risks [23]. However, the understanding of faults, errors and failures depends on cultural aspects peculiar to the application domain (specifying their definitions or meanings). Classification systems, therefore, are tightly coupled with their origin domains and their culture. They are the result of technical as well as socio-political struggles addressed over the years. Another example is the *ACM Computing Classification System*, which resulted from emerging subjects in computing [9]. However, it is possible to figure out that the (sub)classifications of some subjects have echoed the political arguments between different scientific communities. Universities' structures and degrees stress different understandings of scientific and research subjects, which often account for different communities and their socio-political arguments. The socio-political debate over technical arguments depends on the communities involved, their organisational structures, policies and perceptions (of risk) [14]. This debate is still continuing over the shaping of emergent multi- or inter-disciplinarities [28].

Technically, classifications represent (partially) ordered systems consisting of categories, which provide us with "a spatial, temporal or spatio-temporal segmentation of the world" [8]. *Standards* relate to classifications, but differ in the way they are imposed sometimes, resistant to change and adopted by different communities of practice [8]. Communities of practice characterise (or recognise) themselves by adopting or sharing different classifications or standards. Therefore, resulting classifications depend on the mechanisms of shaping them and the policies characterising communities. As risk is a social and collective construct [14], so classifications are too. Classifications, as well as standards, emerge from the negotiation of different communities of practice. They allow information to be spread across organisational boundaries. Classifications, and standards, reside in the intersection between communities of practice. They are *Boundary Objects*, which present those characteristics that allow them to be ubiquitous and pervasive in communities of practice [8]:

> Boundary objects are those objects that both inhabit several communities of practice and satisfy the information requirements of each of them. Boundary objects are thus both plastic enough to adapt to local needs and constraints of the several parties employing them, yet robust enough to maintain a common identity across sites. They are weakly structured in common use and become strongly structured in individual-site use. These objects may be abstract or concrete.

The intersection of different communities of practice, therefore, identifies *Boundary Objects*. Communities of practice recognise shared boundary objects, which capture trade offs between *generality* and *locality*. On the one hand, they capture *explicit knowledge* [29] as generally recognised by communities of practice. On the other hand, they also require *procedural knowledge* [29] in order to make boundary objects effective and available into specific localised situations. Communities of practice tailor them in order to satisfy local requirements. Therefore, boundary objects emerge over time due to *naturalisation* (e.g. cooperation and negotiation) by different communities of practice [8]. The adoption of boundary objects involves the process of naturalisation of the object within communities of practice. Whereas, *membership* to a community of practice requires the recognition of boundary objects as work practices [8]. Similar processes characterise *organisational memory* [1, 2]. Boundary objects require processes of "decontextualisation" and "recontextualisation" that enable organisational memories. Therefore, boundary objects, if suitable processes are in place, are enabling technologies for organisational memories. Boundary objects, as well as technology artefacts, fall short of enabling organisational memory without suitable processes supporting communities of practice. Characterising spatio-temporal dynamics of a classification involves reconstructing its trajectory. *Trajectories* capture the relationships, i.e. membership and naturalisation, between boundary objects and communities of practice [8].

Trajectories characterise the negotiation and shaping of boundary objects between different communities of practice. The negotiation of boundary objects, for instance, the negotiation of different classifications, identifies trajectories as being spatio-temporal ordered representational states [2, 8]. The negotiation process (between communities of practice) needs to address conflicts (e.g. belonging to different categories) arising among different classifications.

The *coupling* between boundary objects and communities of practice depends on the naturalisation of boundary objects within the community of practice as well as of the membership of communities of practice with respect to boundary objects. These relationships create subtle mechanisms of interactions between boundary objects and communities of practice (and themselves, respectively). Boundary objects are pervasive and ubiquitous in communities of practice sharing them. On the one hand, they identify communities of practice. On the other hand, communities of practice identify themselves with boundary objects. Collections of boundary objects and their relationships with communities of practice create *complex* networks of boundary objects, called, *Boundary Infrastructures* [8]. Coupling and complexity of technical systems provide a framework for the characterisation of risk [24]. Similarly, the tight coupling between boundary objects and communities of practice and the complexity of boundary infrastructures emphasise how organisational boundaries represent a hazard or source of risk for technological systems. As structures emerge in technical systems, boundary objects of communities of practice harden the coupling and complexity of such systems. Understanding these structures and the underlying mechanisms that let them emerge highlights boundary objects as enabling technologies for dependability [22]. A review of different case studies allows us to highlight boundary objects and their mechanisms with respect to communities of practice and technological systems. Lack of understanding of boundary objects and failure to take subtle processes and interaction mechanisms into account in designing and deploying new technology represent potential hazards for technological systems. The analysis enhances our ability to understand boundary objects in technological systems and their related risk.

2.2 Patterns of Boundary Infrastructures

Communities of practice tailor classifications, as well as standards, to their knowledge by membership and adopt them by naturalisation. Membership is a complex process of shaping boundary objects. Naturalisation of tools (e.g. classifications) and procedures (e.g. code of practice) is a process of adopting and recognising boundary objects as used within communities of practice. Hence, membership and naturalisation represent two relationships between boundary objects and communities of practices. Membership, on the one hand, from communities of practice to boundary objects, represents procedural knowledge, that is, the process of shaping

Fig. 2.1 Relationships between boundary objects and communities of practice

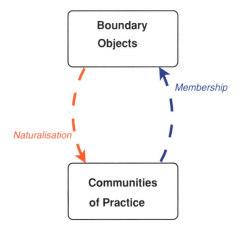

boundary objects by knowledge (e.g. descriptive knowledge) becoming available within communities of practice. Membership identifies boundary objects relevant to communities of practice. Once, for instance, engineering knowledge becomes available due to past experience (e.g. previous design or system failures), communities of practice select and share knowledge to be integrated into boundary objects (e.g. design methodologies and code of practice) [25, 26, 29]. Communities of practice then shape boundary objects by adopting and recognising new available knowledge. On the contrary, naturalisation, from boundary objects to communities of practice, captures the acquisition of general knowledge, embedded into boundary objects, as well as its contextualisation within communities of practice. Naturalisation consists of that process, from boundary objects to communities of practice, which characterises the adoption of boundary objects by communities of practice. The more communities of practice identify themselves with boundary objects, the more boundary objects became natural and pervasive in their usage. In other words, the adoption of boundary objects makes them natural (or nonintrusive) within communities of practice, who identify themselves with boundary objects. It is necessary to familiarise, acquire and use those characterising boundary objects in order to become a member of a community of practice. Figure 2.1 shows the two relationships as directed functions.

Boundary objects, therefore, capture knowledge distribution and coordination processes. They allow us to structure the analysis of organisational knowledge and the identification of related hazards. The investigation of technology innovation with respect to boundary objects identifies a class of technological hazards related to boundary objects, hence, *Boundary Hazards*. Our review of relevant case studies provides examples of Boundary Hazards and their identification.

Fig. 2.2 Mirrored organisations in terms of boundary objects and communities of practice

2.2.1 Standardisation

Organisational strategies often adopt standards and standardisation processes in order to achieve an increased level of control, hence predictability, over production processes and product features. The analysis of a transfer of knowledge between production sites highlights contingencies undermining the effectiveness of standardisation as organisational strategy [16]. One of the case studies in [16] reports the transfer of production processes between two manufacturing sites in the computing sectors. In order to increase its capabilities, a computer organisation acquired a production company, which was also critical for its know-how. It was initially considered the source of the transfer of knowledge because of its high-quality products. Although the two sites, i.e. the computer organisation and the production company, were located in different countries, the overall objective of the acquisition was to increase productivity as well as product quality.

The initial organisational strategy was to replicate standard production processes. This standardisation of production processes was perceived as a successful transfer of knowledge. The basic idea was to have two replicated processes strongly coordinated and coupled together. The production processes were replicated in order to transfer know-how from one site to the other. This would have enabled the two manufacturing sites to maintain, on the one hand, control over the production processes, on the other hand, predictable product reliability. The underlying assumption, later proved to be misplaced, was that highly standardised processes were strongly related to product quality characteristics (e.g. reliability), hence, they could have enabled the delivery of quality product. The initial standardisation strategy intended to reduce diversity between the two manufacturing sites by creating strong correspondences between them. This would have enabled the organisation to deliver products of predictable quality regardless of the production site. However, this proved problematic and gave rise to several issues. Figure 2.2 shows the relationships between the production sites in terms of boundary objects.

Process standardisation was imposed over the communities of practice. There was correspondence, in terms of adopted production artefacts and processes, between the two manufacturing sites. This relationship was obtained and forced by replicating production processes as well as organisational structures. It intended to maintain mutual-correspondences between contextualised knowledge, or boundary objects. Both sites, in terms of boundary objects, adopted the same organisational artefacts and procedures. These boundary objects supposedly provided and maintained coordination between the two sites, although local work practices differed.

The overall goal was to reduce organisational diversity, although the outcome was the opposite. The standardisation process imposed over the two sites emphasised cultural differences between them. Despite the coordination between the two sites, the reflection strategy emphasised differences between the two sites resulting in increased diversity. On the one hand, one production site, the originator, had a strong culture of personal commitment, which allowed a flexible production process with work-around strategies for tackling issues and unforeseen events. This flexible work organisation perceived the other site, the recipient, as over-bureaucratic with its commitment to standardised processes. On the other hand, the recipient organisation perceived few standardised processes, relying on uncodified work practices, as a hazard and potential source of undependabilities. The reflection strategy between the two sites resulted in *mistrust* between the two organisations. The two sites (in particular, the recipient organisation) perceived a *lack of trust*. Hence, they interpreted, the increased control and reduced flexibility were introduced in order to monitor their production activities, respectively. As a consequence of the striking differences, the two production sites requested many changes in order to adapt the standardised process to their local needs. Although the overall process was similar, local work practices were different. These changes and adaptations exposed the alignment of the two sites to increased diversity.

System diversity is, in general, related to properties of *robustness* and *fault tolerance* [20]. Diversity is in principle a 'good' property to have. Unfortunately, extending diversity to other system abstractions (e.g. diversity in safety or dependability cases [6, 21], diversity in organisations) or units of analysis presents some contingencies with respect to dependability. Controversially, diversity might expose organisations to subtle socio-technical hazards.

The overall objectives of the standardisation strategy considered this increased diversity between the two sites to be a failure of the transfer of knowledge. Moreover, due to the instability and unpredictability during the standardisation process, the organisation stopped any project aimed at product or process improvement. Questions, therefore, arise on reflection strategies and diversity with respect to organisations: *How does diversity relate to organisations? How does diversity expose organisations to hazards across organisational boundaries?*

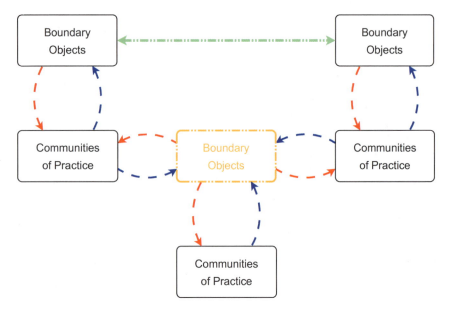

Fig. 2.3 Enhanced standardisation process

2.2.1.1 Restructuring Boundary Infrastructures

The organisation, in order to address the issues arising with the transfer of knowledge, implemented an overall process for controlling and monitoring the replication and contextualisation of the production processes in the two sites, respectively. A joint committee was established for the supervision and coordination of the standardisation process. The committee was responsible for the "exception approval process". This process implemented a change management policy and process dealing with all requests for changes now needing formal approval by the committee. Besides the change management process, the committee identified a set of rules in order to create a shared common understanding of work practices between the two sites. The restructuring introduced shared boundary objects (i.e. change management policies and processes) among common work practices. The implementation of these mitigation actions changed the overall organisation (i.e. structure) of the transfer of knowledge. Figure 2.3 shows the restructuring, in terms of boundary objects, of the organisational transfer of knowledge.

The standardisation process required additional change management policies and processes in order to increase the level of control over local adaptations and understand organisational diversities. The two sites, together with the joint committee, shared the new change management policies and processes with respect to local changes. This allowed the organisation to mitigate issues arising from standardisation. This increased control and understanding over the production sites, although it was initially perceived as a means of controlling and assessing performances of the recipient site. The perception was of lack of trust on local work practices. In a competitive effort, the recipient site exploited the reporting process as a means to gain control over the changes imposed to their work practices. This inhibited any process and product improvement during the transfer of knowledge.

2.2.2 Adopting Generic Technology

Another organisational strategy, often adopted, is the one of introducing and deploying generic technology, for instance, consisting of *Commercial-Off-The-Shelf* (COTS) products. The rationale behind a COTS strategy varies from the goal of reducing labour cost by automation to increasing the level of standardisation in work practices, coordinating different units or divisions of labour, capturing organisational knowledge into technology and so forth. This strategy seems often the most cost-effective and suitable solution, although it presents many pitfalls that may jeopardise any successful deployment as well as organisational effectiveness. Moreover, organisations often adopt generic technology, which misleadingly advocates 'innovation' of production processes with the introduction of new technology. A study in [16] of the introduction of generic technology highlights how the strategy of delegating organisational knowledge to software systems [11–13] may affect communities of practice [10], hence, work practices. Another study in [16] reports on the adoption of general technology in order to standardise work practices within a manufacturing organisation in the automotive domain. The overall objective was to integrate different communities of practice by the introduction of a generic COTS system, i.e. *Product Data Manager* (PDM) software. This would have enabled the technological innovation of organisational production processes and information infrastructures. The organisation, initially, relied on different artefacts, or boundary objects, capturing local knowledge and work practices. The production engineering workflow consisted of subsequent phases capturing organisational procedures [11, 12]. The production process, therefore, involved different boundary objects capturing diverse organisational knowledge. In other words, boundary objects enabled the production process as organisational knowledge or memory [1, 2].

Boundary objects, in order to support organisational memory effectively, need to be flexible general artefacts [8]. The process of *decontextualisation* allows boundary objects to enable organisational memory. Boundary objects capture explicit organisational knowledge [29] and make it available for reuse [1, 2]. Vice versa, the process of *recontextualisation* allows boundary objects to enable organisational memory in use [1, 2]. Procedural knowledge [29] enriches boundary objects and make them available to communities of practice. These processes also take place in the introduction of software technology in order to capture organisational memory. Software technology influences both *organisational declarative memory* and *organisational procedural memory* [12].

Therefore, the adoption of general (software) technology in order to capture organisational knowledge has several implications for the organisation too. The charac-

Fig. 2.4 Disruptive
integration of different
boundary objects

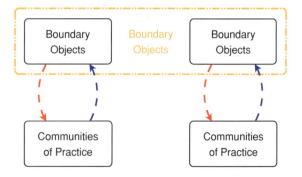

terisation in terms of boundary objects points out organisational memory, on the
one hand, as an artefact having distinct identity and status, on the other hand, as a
process exploiting specific expertise and knowledge. Production involved the translation and coordination from one artefact to the next one in the process. This was
time-consuming and error-prone due to the manual and localised translation and
coordination work involved. However, the production process consisted of different
stages corresponding to different artefacts, respectively, representing the product
trajectory. Boundary objects highlight technology trajectories capturing the different
stages of the production process. Different boundary objects enabled the interaction
of different communities of practice [10]. Digital artefacts or models enabled the
collaboration and interaction between, for instance, industrial design, engineering
and analysis. Different artefacts supported the interaction of different communities
of practices, although they pointed out cultural differences. Processes and artefacts
seemed compatible at a general level. However, local knowledge embedded into work
practices emphasises contextualised skills and expertise. Figure 2.4 shows, in terms
of boundary objects, the adoption of a general technology as an integrated repository
for different work practices and knowledge.

Similar findings highlighted critical issues in adopting general technology for
enabling the collaboration, coordination and integration of different organisational units [11, 12]. The reported studies in [16] highlight critical contingencies in generic technology as enabling organisational memory. Different
communities of practice were using different artefacts in order to support
configuration management at design and production phases respectively.
Both communities of practice were using structural representations in order
to capture different system configurations. The structured representations
captured local knowledge and work practices. Differences between encoding
artefacts, such as diagrammatic representations [15], highlight different work
practices and knowledge. The integration of diverse artefacts involves the risk
of disrupting work practices by highlighting differences and inconsistencies.

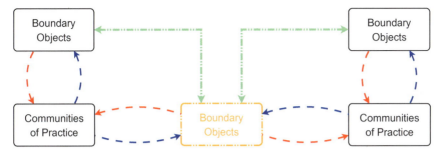

Fig. 2.5 Mediated boundary objects

2.2.2.1 Mitigating Conflicting Knowledge

Generic technology may integrate and substitute existing artefacts, or boundary objects. It, however, requires the identification of coding and decoding procedures (e.g. contextualisation and recontextualisation) in order to support existing work practices, often capturing diverse knowledge, expertise and culture. A lack of support for these processes affects the effective deployment of new technology as innovation strategy. Loosely coupled work practices and technology provide limited support for existing organisational knowledge and procedures. Organisational procedures carry critical knowledge that effectively deals with (or mitigates) design faults or knowledge discrepancies. The introduction of new technology faces these issues, which take the form of failures, process inefficiencies or conflicting culture and work practices. Beside the introduction of new technology, therefore, it is necessary to identify those processes mediating and coordinating existing knowledge embedded in current work practices. Figure 2.5 shows the mediation of local knowledge with respect to communities of practice adopting different, maybe, conflicting, boundary objects.

Processes of coding and decoding local knowledge would allow new generic technology to articulate current work practices. These processes represent boundary objects enabling the coordination of local work practices and the mitigation of conflicting knowledge. They involve negotiations between communities of practice, who would, eventually, acquire new knowledge configurations by alternating processes of membership and naturalisation. New technology indirectly relates to existing organisational knowledge coded in naturalised boundary objects. Membership allows communities of practice to fix arising discrepancies into boundary objects. Whereas, naturalisation, the other way around, allows communities of practice to familiarise themselves with emerging knowledge configurations. The underlying mechanisms (in terms of boundary objects, communities of practice, and processes of naturalisation and membership) highlight the *co-evolutionary* nature of introducing new technology into work practices. The evolutionary process may eventually stabilise and emerge as new boundary objects and communities of practice, respectively. The temptation is to enable this evolutionary cycle into new technology. However, it requires communities of practice to naturalise new boundary objects, which could collide due to conflicting knowledge.

2.2.3 Creating Organisational Infrastructures

Complex organisations, such as the ones in the healthcare domain, are often restructuring their infrastructures in order to support diverse challenging competitive objectives (e.g. dependability and performance) and innovations of their processes [27]. The case study in [3, 16] looks at how an organisation in the healthcare domain intends to integrate its information infrastructure. Originally, the information infrastructure consisted of a variety of localised systems and work practices providing and supporting the gathering of patient data.

A central Medical Records unit reporting directly to management was responsible for the maintenance, that is, the coordination and integration, of the different information arising from work practices. This organisation relies on a hierarchical allocation of responsibilities and divisions of labour. The integration of different existing classification systems, or information infrastructures, in a healthcare domain highlights difficulties and contingencies of standardisation strategies advocating general (COTS) technology to fit all work practices [3, 16]. The overall objective is twofold. First, the new system intends to integrate the different systems currently in use across the organisation. Second, the system aims to provide further management control by retrieving comparable data and statistics about different services. On the one hand, the integrated information system was concerned with the improvement of patient care and the accuracy, timeliness and completeness of information used within the organisation for clinical and administrative decision-making. Management was, therefore, particularly concerned that the new system should provide a means for increasing control over performance. This was perceived as a technology innovation enabling the achievement of organisational targets. On the other hand, the integrated information system intended to support work practices by the availability of data providing feedback for research purposes. This would have enabled the various units to move towards evidence-based clinical practices. Figure 2.6, from an organisational viewpoint, shows the emerging organisational information infrastructure consisting of different communities of practice familiar with boundary objects naturalised over several years of experiences.

The case study in [3, 16] analyses the introduction of an integrated *Patient Information Management System* (PIMS) across different heterogeneous units. The system is to provide three main functionalities: (1) it records patient information; (2) it allows users to retrieve historical information about their work practices;

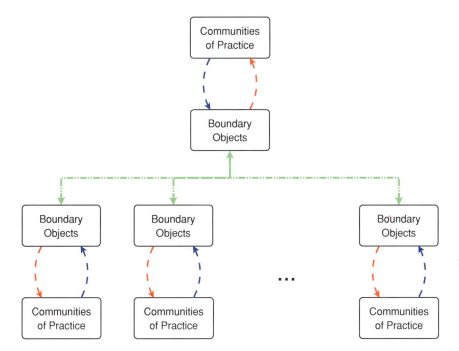

Fig. 2.6 Emerging organisational information infrastructure

(3) finally, the system allows users to analyse data in order to support decision-making and evidence-based clinical practices. The study focused on one component, namely, the *Contact Purpose Menu*, of the new system [3, 16]. It allows users to select among different options from a pull-down menu of activity descriptions. The field is mandatory for each clinical contact. The menu's customisation and evolution proved to be critical for the creation of an integrated information infrastructure. The initial version of the menu simply integrated different options from different existing menus, assuming that the meaning of each option would have been shared among different users and across organisational boundaries and divisions of labour. Figure 2.7 shows some of the categories (forming a classification system) drawn from the contact purpose menu [3].

The move towards an integrated information system represented a shift in *responsibility*. The new integrated information system now requires that members of clinical staff are responsible for data entry relating to patient care. This means that they are now accountable for the *integrity* and *validity* of the information provided. The direct allocation of responsibility and *accountability* over clinical staff increased the perception and the pressure of management control over performances of work practices. Moreover, clinical staff were, forcibly, required to use a tool which poorly reflected local work practices. Heterogeneous artefacts, for instance, paper-based records, often carry on useful information for the smooth coordination of collabo-

Fig. 2.7 Categories in a
contact purpose menu

```
Assessment
Case conference
Challenging behaviour
Cognitive behavioural therapy
Depot medication
Detox
Discharge
Enabling
Epilepsy
Follow-up
Full assessment
Health promotion
Initial assessment
Lawyer/solicitor report
Maintenance
Management
Mental health assessment
Methadone contract signing
Methadone programme
Methadone review
Not specified
Other report
...
```

rations.[2] This is clear from a close look at how clinical staff often organise work practices and clinical judgement in health care. Therefore, the introduction of new tools, such as *Integrated Care Records*, should take into account how to support existing work practices without being disruptive [17]. Unfortunately, such issues arose in the case of PIMS [3, 16]. Figure 2.8 shows how different local systems, artefacts, or boundary objects, were tentatively integrated into the new system. The strategy was one of forcing integration and standardisation across organisational boundaries and divisions of labour, that is, across communities of practice.

The integration was problematic. Clinical users reported difficulties in selecting the available options. They struggled to make sense of the definitions. Moreover, they reported differences with the old system(s). For instance, an old system allowed them to select multiple options for each contact. These problems highlighted how the new system poorly reflected heterogeneous work practices.

Although the system allowed users to select a generic "Not Specified" option, further system usage analysis pointed out that the users were selecting this option rarely. This further stressed the struggle of users in understanding the meanings of the different options. They feared the new system misrepresented and poorly captured

---

[2] Processes of organisational memory highlight how process trajectories involve "many small memories" [2], or artefacts, capturing the various representational states. Distributed cognition allows the analysis of diverse artefacts, or boundary objects, used in practice in order to accomplish a specific task. For instance, the study in [2] analyses the work practices of a telephone hotline group. Work practices use various artefacts forming the process trajectory—"that representational states take through various memories as an individual process, there are actually multiple group and organizational processes occurring." [2]

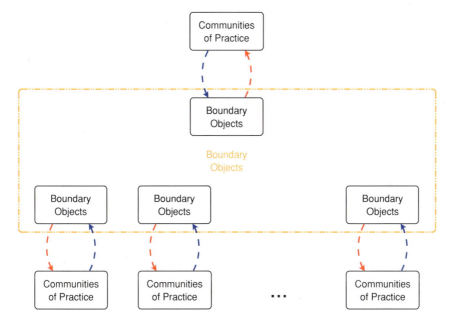

Fig. 2.8 COTS organisational infrastructure

their work practices. Moreover, the figures originated by the system present the hazard of being misleaded in order to support organisational decision-making. This, somehow, affected *trust* between organisational management and local units. The clinical staff perceived a lack of trust in their professional practices and expertise. Establishing the relationship between the general categories optioned by the system and local work practices highlighted the organisational dependency on clinical data. This relationship, once degraded, is a major source of contingencies affecting organisational dependability and performance.

2.2.3.1 Classifying Work Practices

The case study highlights the difficulties in designing and implementing information infrastructures [3, 16]. It questions the underlying assumptions of advocating the delivery of new technology in order to standardise and integrate heterogeneous (local) work practices. It points out that this strategy carries uncertainties, contingencies and hazards. The reported experience illustrates the issues and obstacles of creating an integrated information system, or boundary infrastructure, as opposed to several local information systems, or boundary objects, emerging as a (patchy) information system or boundary infrastructure.

The implementation of localised information systems would be a strategy in order to progressively achieve an organisation-wide information infrastructure supporting different communities of practice. The integration phase would, then, commence once these local systems had been successfully deployed. This provides several consequential benefits. First, organisations can structure and manage information in locally meaningful ways. This aims to maximise the usefulness of the information, ensuring local meanings. Local adaptations are possible and remain local. Second, it allows organisations to delay design decisions about information provided across organisational boundaries or divisions of labour. This, moreover, supports negotiation over any shift of responsibility and accountability for information shared across organisational infrastructures. Third, the costs of sharing information are spread over the different communities of practice adopting related boundary objects. It is necessary, however, to identify trade-offs among such benefits and the costs of maintaining audit and verification with dispersed information practices. Contingencies between trust and dependability may arise due to perceived risk associated with the adoption of new boundary objects.

Shift in responsibility and poorly reflected work practices account for user dissatisfaction of new artefacts. The case study highlights that system design and deployment need to consider work practices progressively. That is, the design and deployment processes need to learn how work practices rely on localised artefacts, or boundary objects. It is a process of learning and adaptation, rather than imposing standardised boundary objects that are meaningless when delivered in other contexts. Moreover, it is evident how information is context sensitive. Information makes sense in local contexts or work practices. The creation of an integrated information infrastructure should be conducted alongside the identification of procedures (e.g. contextualisation, decontextualisation and recontextualisation [1, 2]) to translate knowledge. These procedures, on the one hand, allow information to be generalised in order to acquire a shared meaning across organisational boundaries, on the other hand, they allow information to be adapted and enriched in order to make it useful to local work practices and objectives [3].

The study highlights issues in the deployment and use of information systems across heterogeneous communities of practice [3, 16]. These issues represent sources of undependabilities for the success of technology innovation and the effectiveness of organisational practice. Improved awareness allows organisations to minimise and mitigate such problems when implementing this type of system. Moreover, the analysis of *Boundary Hazards* helps to identify the areas where difficulties can be expected to arise. It is possible to identify three distinctive critical activities [3, 16] involved in defining and deploying a classification of work practices in an organisational setting.

1. *Constructing a classification* involves both amalgamating the local classifications, which arise within the communities of practice. Moreover, at the level of the overall classification, it considers example cases and how they fit into the classification.
2. *Using the classification* captures the practice of classifying cases as they arise in the course of everyday work. This requires the understanding of process trajectories as shaped by the classification.
3. *Analysing informationin classes* involves the construction of statistical analysis over the classified data.

Each of these different activities engages with different communities of practice to varying extents. Different communities of practice have different concerns and needs for support in their activities.

2.3 Boundary Hazards

Developing and implementing new organisational information systems necessarily involves reaching agreement, implicitly or tacitly, about knowledge. Various decisions affect how to classify information, how to represent it through the choice of boundary objects and how to access it. Detailed focus upon the design, implementation and use of information systems allows us to consider various opportunities that may exist either in terms of improved change management procedures or systems to deploy information systems effectively and dependably. Organisations adopt different strategies in order to deal with similar problems with respect to information infrastructures, or boundary objects (infrastructures). Technology solutions address this problem differently, sometimes locally or, alternatively, at an organisational level. In other cases, organisations adopt existing solutions as established standards or classification systems. However, transfer of knowledge, from its local origin to a standardised classification, or across organisational boundaries and divisions of labour, may affect local knowledge and undermine currently existing work practices. Organisations failing to understand and to treat carefully boundary objects (infrastructures) are likely to experience disruptive consequences, which represent significant threats to the dependability of information systems. These hazards may affect knowledge with potential critical consequences for organisational activities and objectives. Technology integration and standardisation, or innovation strategies, although they often involve solutions (e.g. COTS systems) outside direct scrutiny, expose organisations to a set of hazards (across organisational boundaries or divisions of labour) involving boundary objects, or infrastructures, hence *Boundary Hazards*. Table 2.1 summarises and describes the different Boundary Hazards identified by the case studies.

Table 2.1 Boundary hazards

Hazard	Description
Exposed diversity	The restructuring of boundary objects (or introduction and creation of new ones), or boundary infrastructures, exposes organisational diversities. On the one hand, it highlights diversities across organisational boundaries in terms of work practices and knowledge. On the other hand, standardisation reduces organisational diversity
Conflicting knowledge	Integrating or merging different boundary objects embodying local knowledge highlights conflicting knowledge or differences among communities of practice
Lack of coordination	Boundary objects stretch organisational deficiencies in coordinating transfer of knowledge
Shift in responsibility	Boundary objects, or boundary infrastructures, allocate responsibilities across organisational structures and divisions of labour. Changes in organisational boundaries, due to changes in boundary objects, result in shifts in responsibilities
Loose coupling	Boundary objects expose loose coupling, between work practice and knowledge, misrepresenting communities of practice
Mistrust (or lack of trust)	Communities of practice perceive the use of boundary objects in order to centralise control over work practices as a lack of trust. They develop mistrust across integrated boundary objects
Lack of cooperation (or competitive behaviour)	Different communities of practice develop competitive behaviour, or lack of cooperation, in order to gain control over boundary objects and exert their policies (power) over others

Comparing the very different organisational settings of health care and high-technology industries highlighted the influence of sustained efforts geared towards technological innovation, formalisation and standardisation activities in different domains. The case studies analysed problems of working with and evolving classifications of work procedures, which are central to the organisational objectives of new systems. They concerned the need to address the dynamics of standardisation (encompassing both the formation and implementation of standardisation). The analyses allow us to reflect on the methodological implications of needing to address *Boundary Hazards* concerning designing and evolving technology innovation. The results draw attention to the contradictory implications of standardisation efforts. Standardisation faces discrepancies between standard schemes and local practices, which are rooted in existing heterogeneous information structures. It can yield a sense of increasing general accountability, scrutiny and control over distant activities. This can also result in a loss of local focus and detail oversight. The visible alignment process thus initiated may, at least in the short term, encounter or set into play resistance in the organisation. This may be a source of new undependabilities. The contradictory effects of standardisation efforts go to the heart of questions of trust, in particular, to the (misplaced) assumption that standardised information structures and practices can resolve the problems of trust in complex and (spatially and culturally) dispersed organisational settings.

2.3.1 Addressing Boundary Hazards

The investigation of *Boundary Hazards* highlights different strategies as contingency actions mitigating the technological risk related to evolving boundary objects or infrastructures.

- *Restructuring boundary infrastructures* addresses the issues arising with loose coupled boundary objects and work practices. It allows increased controlling and monitoring over the adoption and local tailoring of boundary objects. This enables communities of practice, on the one hand, to shape boundary objects according to their local needs, on the other hand, to naturalise emerging boundary objects in their work practices.
- *Mitigating conflicting knowledge* concerns the integration of different boundary objects. It allows organisations to address inconsistencies of knowledge across organisational boundaries. It involves processes of coordination and translation between local and general knowledge characterising boundary objects adopted by communities of practices.
- *Classifying work practices* captures local knowledge embedded in work practices and relevant boundary objects, which translate across organisational boundaries in a difficult way. Moreover, it takes account of responsibility shifts, which are due to misrepresentation (into boundary objects) of work practices.

It is possible to draw two sets of recommendations. The first concerns information system designers. The challenge now is how to design systems that support diversity in culture and work practices. Beside acknowledging work practices, design needs also to support local flexibility while at the same time continuing to perform a strong coordinating and integrating function. Hence, designers also need to conceive systems that enable an organisation to align with evolving objectives over time.

The second set of recommendations concerns management practice. The challenge in this case is the need to enforce standards while taking into account the different levels and types of diversities and needs for differentiation that are specific to each individual organisational context. The principal challenge for managers remains to identify trade offs between specialised ad hoc solutions and general ready-available ones (e.g. COTS systems). Moreover, any decision affects the level of pervading of boundary objects into work practices. This also affects the extent of coordination and control over communities of practice. These strategies and recommendations provide guidelines for organisational practices and future research.

References

1. Ackerman MS, Halverson CA (2000) Reexamining organizational memory. Commun ACM 43(1):59–64. doi:10.1145/323830.323845
2. Ackerman MS, Halverson CA (2004) Organizational memory as objects, processes, and trajectories: an examination of organizational memory in use. Comput Support Coop Work 13(2):155–189. doi:10.1023/B:COSU.0000045805.77534.2a
3. Anderson S, Hardstone G, Procter R, Williams R (2008) Down in the (data)base(ment): supporting configuration in organisational information systems. In: Ackerman MS, Halverson CA, Erickson T, Kellogg WA (eds) Resources, co-evolution, and artifacts: theory in CSCW, computer supported cooperative work. Springer, London, pp 221–253. doi:10.1007/978-1-84628-901-9_9
4. Avižienis A, Laprie J-C, Randell B, Landwehr C (2004) Basic concepts and taxonomy of dependable and secure computing. IEEE Trans Dependable Secur Comput 1(1):11–33. doi:10.1109/TDSC.2004.2
5. Beck U (1992) Risk society: towards a new modernity. SAGE Publications, London
6. Bloomfield R, Littlewood B (2003) Multi-legged arguments: the impact of diversity upon confidence in dependability arguments. In: Proceedings of the 2003 international conference on dependable systems and networks, DSN'03, IEEE Computer Society, pp 25–34. doi:10.1109/DSN.2003.1209913
7. Bowker GC (1996) The history of information infrastructures: the case of the international classification of diseases. Inf Process Manag 32(1):49–61. doi:10.1016/0306-4573(95)00049-M
8. Bowker GC, Star SL (1999) Sorting things out: classification and its consequences. The MIT Press, Cambridge
9. Coulter N (1997) ACM's computing classification system reflects changing times. Commun ACM 40(12):111–112. doi:10.1145/265563.265579
10. D'Adderio L (2001) Crafting the virtual prototype: how firms integrate knowledge and capabilities across organisational boundaries. Res Policy 30(9):1409–1424. doi:10.1016/S0048-7333(01)00159-7
11. D'Adderio L (2002) Configuring software, reconfiguring memories: the influence of integrated systems on knowledge storage, retrieval and reuse. In: Proceedings of the 2002 ACM symposium on applied computing, SAC 2002, ACM, pp 726–731. doi:10.1145/508791.508932
12. D'Adderio L (2003) Configuring software, reconfiguring memories: the influence of integrated systems on the reproduction of knowledge and routines. Ind Corp Chang 12(2):321–350
13. D'Adderio L (2003) Inside the virtual product: how organisations create knowledge through software. Edward Elgar, Cheltenham
14. Douglas M, Wildavsky A (1982) Risk and culture: an essay on the selection of technological and environmental dangers. University of California Press, Berkeley
15. Gurr C, Hardstone G (2001) Implementing configurable information systems: a combined social science and cognitive science approach. In: Beynon M, Nehaniv CL, Dautenhahn K (eds) Proceedings of CT 2001, no. 2117 in LNAI. Springer, Heidelberg, pp 391–404. doi:10.1007/3-540-44617-635

16. Hardstone G, D'Adderio L, Williams R (2006) Standardization, trust and dependability. In: Clarke K, Hardstone G, Rouncefield M, Sommerville I (eds) Trust in technology: a socio-technical perspective, computer supported cooperative work, vol 36, chap 4. Springer, London pp 69–103. doi:10.1007/1-4020-4258-2_4

17. Hardstone G, Hartswood M, Procter R, Slack R, Voss A, Rees G (2004) Supporting informality: team working and integrated care records. In: Proceedings of the 2004 ACM conference on computer supported cooperative work, CSCW'04, ACM, pp 142–151. doi:10.1145/1031607.1031632

18. Hughes, AC, Hughes, TP (eds) (2000) Systems, experts, and computers: the systems approach in management and engineering, world war II and after. The MIT Press, Cambridge

19. Johnson CW (2003) Failure in safety-critical systems: a handbook of accident and incident reporting. University of Glasgow Press, Scotland

20. Littlewood B, Popov P, Strigini L (2001) Modeling software design diversity: a review. ACM Comput Surv 33(2):177–208. doi:10.1145/384192.384195

21. Littlewood B, Wright D (2007) The use of multi-legged arguments to increase confidence in safety claims for software-based systems: a study based on a BBN analysis of an idealised example. IEEE Trans on Softw Eng 33(5):347–365. doi:10.1109/TSE.2007.1002

22. Lutters WG, Ackerman MS (2002) Achieving safety: a field study of boundary objects in aircraft technical support. In: Proceedings of the 2002 ACM conference on computer supported cooperative work, CSCW '02, ACM Press, pp 266–275. doi:10.1145/587078.587116

23. Neumann PG (1995) Computer related risks. The ACM Press, New York

24. Perrow C (1999) Normal accidents: living with high-risk technologies. Princeton University Press, New Jersey

25. Petroski H (1982) To engineer is human: the role of failure in successful design. Vintage Books, New York

26. Petroski H (1994) Design paradigms: case histories of error and judgment in engineering. Cambridge University Press, New York

27. Robertson B, Sribar V (2002) The adaptive enterprise: IT infrastructure strategies to manage change and enable growth. IT best practice series. Addison-Wesley, Boston

28. Rogers Y, Scaife M, Rizzo A (2005) Interdisciplinarity: an emergent or engineered process? In: Derry SJ, Schunn CD, Gernsbacher MA (eds) Interdisciplinary collaboration: an emerging cognitive science, Lawrence Erlbaum Associates, Mahwah

29. Vincenti WG (1990) What engineers know and how they know it: analytical studies from aeronautical history. The Johns Hopkins University Press, Baltimore

30. WHO (2004) Report for the consultation meeting on the WHO business plan for classifications, final report edn. World Health Organization (WHO)

31. WHO (2004) World Health Organization—family of international classifications. World Heath Organization (WHO)

32. WHO (2005) WHO business plan for classifications, version 1.0 edn. World Heath Organization (WHO)

33. WHO (2011) History of the development of the ICD. World Health Organization (WHO)

Chapter 3
Technological Evolution

Social interactions, shaping technology, allow us to investigate how technology pervades work practices, hence, understanding communities of practice with respect to technology. On the one hand, social shaping of technology highlights risk perception of technological evolution. On the other hand, technological evolution is a potential hazard, disruptive, for work practices. However, it is possible to analyse and capture technology trajectories in order to understand, with respect to technological evolution, design decisions and activities enabling engineering knowledge growth. The review of different case studies uncovers multidisciplinary aspects of technology innovation. It highlights complex interactions affecting our ability to support technology evolution, hence, technology innovation.

3.1 Evolutionary Observations

Knowledge growth in engineering characterises epistemic accounts of technological innovation [44]. Emerging technological risk relates to *uncertainty* in *engineering design knowledge* [44] with respect to technical as well as environmental factors (e.g. social organisations, communities of practice, evolving operational profiles, increasing performance requirements), although knowledge uncertainty provides a partial account of technological risk [14]. An evolutionary *variation-selection model* for design [44] captures, to some extent, the growth of engineering knowledge. The variation-selection model involves three basic cognitive activities, which characterise engineering knowledge and its growth. First, searching for past experiences in which engineering knowledge was successfully used. Note that, in searching from past experience, failures represent a source of engineering knowledge too [36, 37]. Second, the conceptual incorporation of engineering knowledge into local artefacts. This highlights two features of engineering knowledge. Engineering knowledge is the result of communities of practice, that is, the *social shaping of technology* [30]. It also emphasises knowledge as *distributed cognition* [34], that is, cognition relies on knowledge distributed over diverse artefacts which communities of practice adopt

S. Anderson and M. Felici, *Emerging Technological Risk*,
DOI: 10.1007/978-1-4471-2143-5_3, © Springer-Verlag London Limited 2012

(or naturalise). Therefore, knowledge is the result of communities of practice adopting artefacts (or boundary objects). It is necessary to select those design solutions that are likely to function in future (foreseen) operational conditions. It is evident how uncertainty in engineering design knowledge involves an extent of risk.

Evolutionary design processes intend, to some extent, to address knowledge growth, uncertainty and three main underlying *evolutionary drivers* (or, *drivers of technology evolution*): *functional failure*, *presumptive anomaly* and the need to *reduce uncertainty* in engineering design knowledge [44]. Functional failures characterise increasing performance requirements under unforeseen operational conditions. *Failures*, or *errors*, represent a source of engineering knowledge [36, 37], although design faults represent a threat for system dependability [5]. The evolutionary process of searching from knowledge and designing innovations benefits from the analysis of past design faults. Growth in engineering design knowledge is therefore a compound learning process (e.g. *social learning* involves *learning by interacting* or *learning by doing* with respect to technology [48]). Organisations often advocate technology innovation as a means of improving performance (e.g. increased safety). Unfortunately, uncontrolled and misunderstood introduction of new technology could have controversial results in complex application domains.

The introduction of new technology increases risk-tacking attitudes or behaviours in some safety-critical domains. Avionics and Air Traffic Management (ATM) industries, for instance, need to fulfil an increasing demand for cost-effective services and performances (e.g. in terms of increasing number of accommodated flights and decreasing number of loss-of-separation between aircraft as increased safety levels). The introduction of new technology may have controversial results, because it increases the demands on safety and performance. Organisations justify with technology innovation their increasing demands over performance and safety targets, although technological risk remains stable, or increases. This explains, to some extent, why risk perception has remained unchanged in Avionics or ATM domains [35]:

> There are some unique structural conditions in this industry that promote safety, and despite complexity and coupling, technological fixes can work in some areas. Yet we continue to have accidents because aircraft and the airways still remain somewhat complex and tightly coupled, but also because those in charge continue to push the system to its limits. Fortunately, the technology and the skilled pilots and air traffic controllers remain a bit ahead of the pressures, and the result has been that safety has continued to increase, though not as markedly as in earlier decades.

Technology innovation can, for instance, induce risk-taking behaviour with a reduction of risk perception favouring phenomena of *risk homeostasis* [23]. Presumptive anomalies highlight uncertainties over future operational conditions or requirements, which may expose the limitations of current systems. Design processes, finally, seek to reduce uncertainty by specific activities (e.g. system testing).

Fig. 3.1 Discovery and innovation cycle relating communities of practice, engineering knowledge and technology

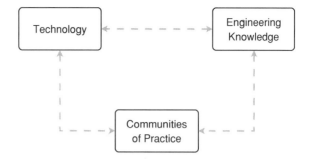

The characterisation of engineering knowledge [44] emphasises that creating knowledge and reducing uncertainty are community activities depending on work practices and (social) interactions. Technology, or engineering knowledge, registers social (e.g. organisational) interactions into structured designs. The *system approach*, for example, highlights how heterogeneous artefacts form and let technology emerge resulting into systems [24]. Engineering knowledge emphasises how technological artefacts emerge as result of design activities giving rise to *technology trajectories*, or what seems to be the "normal" *evolution of technology*, consisting of "subsequent" *technical changes* [31, 32]. On the other hand, sociological accounts of engineering knowledge highlight the social shaping of technology [30]. Social processes of technological change emphasise a notion of *heterogeneous engineering* as (design) solutions in search of problems, rather than problems to be solved or problems in search of solutions [31, 32]. Separating knowledge from technology is just an artificial segmentation for representing cycles of discoveries and innovations. Figure 3.1 represents a discovery and innovation cycle in terms of engineering knowledge resulting in technology adopted by communities of practice.

The innovation cycle provides a conceptual framework for capturing and analysing technological evolution with respect to *engineering knowledge, technology* and *communities of practice*. Communities of practice shape technology innovation by selecting and adopting available technology and knowledge. Eliminating the relation of communities of practice with respect to technology and (engineering) knowledge restrict the understanding of discovery and innovation to classical engineering deterministic views giving rise to the controversial *paradox of proving the correctness of technology* [29]. In what follows, we analyse different case studies, which allow us to review and instantiate examples of technology innovation in terms of communities of practice, technology trajectories and engineering knowledge. Our analysis identifies a class of socio-technical hazards that concern technological evolution, hence, *Evolutionary Hazards*.

3.2 Evolving Practices

Technology innovation involves activities creating and enabling engineering knowledge [44]. On the one hand, engineering activities gather knowledge and make it available for designing technology innovation. On the other hand, they foster engineering knowledge within communities of practice. Engineering processes, traditionally, progress and organise technology production in terms of subsequent development phases. Various development processes organise phases differently, although most of them rely on similar basic activities (e.g. requirements elicitation, system design, implementation, maintenance, deployment) and carry different assumptions about how these activities relate to each other.[1] Historically, engineering processes have common origin in the *system approach* [24], which emphasises how heterogeneous parts form technology systems and relate to one another. Various engineering approaches advocate evolutionary development processes in order to tackle hazards and, hence, reduce the risk of technology projects. Evolutionary aspects of production processes mitigate, to some extent, the *volatility* of technology, although they provide limited explanation and understanding of evolution as technology innovation in practice. Despite all emphasis on iterative or evolutionary developments, there are still many concerns and contingencies regarding how to understand and assess technology innovation with respect to (new) application domains: *How does technology innovation fit into work practices? How do communities of practice adopt and perceive technology innovation?* In order to further investigate the evolutionary nature of technology innovation, it is necessary to highlight those mechanisms characterising and supplying technological changes. This requires us to bridge, that is, understand the relationship between, technological design (or technology innovation) and application domains. The main issue is to know what technology is supposed to do and how it relates to work practices (e.g. system usages and operational profiles). However, it is impossible to have complete knowledge of these matters before any technological system is actually designed, implemented and used. The study of bringing technology into use allows us to understand subtle interactions and contingencies between technology innovation and work practices.

Technology innovation introduces changes into work practices. Understanding the underlying mechanisms of innovation requires us to investigate communities of practice and their dynamic boundaries. A process of *co-realisation*, which has origins in the theories of ethnomethodology and participatory design, allows us to cross the boundaries between communities of practice in design and application domains [21]. The paradigm of *learning by doing* enables technology expertise to offer prompt support to communities of practice, or divisions of labour. Vice versa, technology expertise benefits from direct involvements with communities of practice. This allows sharing knowledge about work practices and contingencies

---

[1] *Software engineering* processes, for instance, involve the activities of *software specification, design, implementation, validation* and *evolution* [42]. Process models (e.g. *waterfall, spiral*) organise and relate phases to each other differently (according to underlying assumptions and application domain constraints).

characterising specific application domains, as opposed to looking at domain representations, abstractions or ethnographic descriptions. It enables communication between communities of practice in order to investigate divisions of labour (e.g. in terms of responsibilities) in designing technology innovation. It overcomes the boundaries between technology innovation design and use: *How do communities of practice engage collaborative behaviour over technology innovation? How do communities of practice recognise and acknowledge membership?* Investigating dynamics of communities of practice requires an interpretation of technology innovation design in terms of community mechanisms (e.g. naturalisation, membership, knowledge gathering, knowledge sharing).

The principles underlying *co-realisation* support the collaboration between communities of practice, respectively, in design and application domains [21]. That is, they enable collaborations between technology innovation designers (or *facilitators*) and recipients (or users). On the one hand, technology expertise acquires local knowledge and understanding of technology domains, i.e. of communities of practice. This requires technology expertise to naturalise local knowledge (in terms of familiarising with adopted boundary objects), hence, to became a member of a community of practice (in terms of understanding work practices). On the other hand, communities of practice acknowledge specific technology expertise. *Trust* between communities of practice favours cooperative behaviour supporting co-realisation. It allows communities of practice to understand their responsibilities with respect to technology innovation. This is convenient for communities of practice to gain trust in engineering knowledge (e.g. technology expertise) and to perceive technology innovation as less intrusive than being politically and organisationally imposed. This clarifies *accountability* over communities of practice and creates common knowledge with respect to technology innovation. Therefore, co-realisation supports defining, allocating and shifting responsibilities of technology innovation.

Communities of practice, therefore support technology innovation, because they understand related responsibilities. Moreover, trust and cooperation between communities of practice enable exploratory approaches for technology innovation. Communities of practice suggest and support—by processes of membership shaping adopted artefacts and naturalisation acquiring artefacts—further development into technology innovation, thus overcoming the problem of *standardisation* where communities of practice little engage with development activities. Technology expertise (or engineering knowledge), in co-realisation, has therefore the responsibility of implementing, maintaining, operating and changing working technology and its *configuration* in response to evolving work practices. Communities of practice will then responsibly engage in the exploration of different alternative solutions, which may be available and financially possible. Communities of practice, empowered by mutual trust (together with a clear understanding and allocation of responsibilities), develop, perceive and understand the risk of technology innovation.

Therefore, they accept the risk involved with technology innovation. *What then is technology innovation design?* Technology innovation involves enabling engineering knowledge and allocating responsibilities. Communities of practice, then, acquire a critical role in assessing (the benefits of) technology innovation by experience, rather than just assessing compliance with design artefacts (e.g. specifications, models). The collaboration, required by co-realisation processes, between communities of practice supports knowledge communication and sharing. It overcomes the communication problem between communities of practice. Moreover, this is responsive to local needs and able to maintain coupling between technology and evolving practices. This section reviews the application of co-realisation in diverse contexts, in particular, dealing with the effects of changes and the need for intermediary systems between work contexts and large-scale generic software packages, e.g. Commercial-Off-The-Shelf (COTS) systems. The results of adopting co-realisation principles highlight the ability of technology expertise to track change trajectories in local contexts. This enables cooperation of communities of practice within organisations in order to adapt technology and work practices to changes (into trajectories). From a risk perspective viewpoint, co-realisation provides a means to make a wide range of risk visible. This complements technical risk management and provides a mechanism for addressing and managing broad classes of socio-technical hazards.

3.2.1 *Understanding Responsibility*

Technology innovation in complex domains such as healthcare, or medical, carries subtle hazards, which may jeopardise any effort towards introducing new technologies or improvements into work practices. The ethnomethodological study of a medical domain (a toxicology ward) highlights contingencies between work practices and organisational objectives [13, 21, 22]. The study involved a six month period of familiarisation with work practices through fieldwork, which allowed building relationships and understanding of knowledge domain. This follows processes of naturalisation (acquiring local knowledge) by which technology designers become members of communities of practice. Technology designers, after becoming members of communities of practice, have a convenient position for identifying work practices in which technology could provide beneficial innovation. The acquired understanding of work practice points out overall objectives or requirements constraining and pushing the limits of organisational performance. Technical failures are often latent or dormant in complex domains. They may indirectly affect, or emerge as reduced, organisational performance in terms of perceived dissatisfaction or unsatisfactory work practice [21].

Local knowledge and culture, therefore, are essential predicates for technology innovation design. Understanding how work practices address organisational objectives requires co-realisation to unveil opportunities for technology innovation. Technology innovation design, then, requires localised collaborations between technology designers (or facilitators) and users (or domain experts). Technology designers need to acquire and naturalise local knowledge embedded into work practices or domain culture. Group meetings, similar to participatory design projects, discussed potential (alternative) applications. Knowledge communication and sharing are mechanisms for exploring technology alternatives and usages. Moreover, these mechanisms, underlying co-realisation, enable technology designers and users to explore and assess different alternative technologies. Although the exploration of different technology alternatives and their usages may carry some hazards, people are willing to accept the associated risk, because they understand their responsibilities with respect to technology innovation. Responsibility issues and technology requirements arise over subsequent cycles of discussions. These discussions clarify responsibility and infuse trust in the collaboration. The trust in the collaboration, due to the acquisition of a recognised membership within the community of practice, allows technology designers to propose the adoption of technology as innovation. This may require the adaptation and investigation of readily-available technology (e.g. speech recognition system), such as COTS systems.[2] The exploitation and usage of technology innovation give rise to hazards and contingencies with work practices and organisational policies. In particular, technology innovation requires understanding responsibility. It may also imply a shift in responsibility across divisions of labour or organisational boundaries.

3.2.2 Acquiring Trust

Trust in responsibilities provides the foundations for co-realisation mechanisms. These mechanisms emerge as cooperation within application domains. Another application domain, where co-realisation has been adopted, is a manufacturer of mass-produced, customised diesel engines [21]. The extensive application of co-realisation and analysis within a manufacturing domain emphasises how trust enables processes of technology innovation into work practice. Work in the manufacturing plant's control room involves various tasks like monitoring the production process, adjusting parameters, translating between the production process and the work of various other plant staff (e.g. quality control) and so on. It also involves continuous re-organisation and optimisation activities, which are essential to constantly match the plant's work to the constraints of production. The manufacturing organisation, for instance, was characterised by a 'just-in-time' culture embedded in work practice. The provision of components to the assembly line was fundamental in order to guarantee smooth production processes. Although the production presented many unforeseen events and conditions affecting organisational performances, work practice embedded local knowledge in order to deal with such issues. The notion, or classification, of systems as *buildable* was, for instance, over time substituted by a classification of systems as *green*, *orange* and *red* in order to capture the contingen-

---

[2] The acquisition, deployment and use of COTS systems is somehow problematic due to limited accounts of, and guidance for assessing, human factors [12].

cies and hazards associated with missing components [46]. Although this practice shifted responsibilities from monitoring systems to people, they accepted the associated risk because it was possible to deal with specific situations according to local knowledge and past experience.

The co-location of technology designers, or facilitators, with communities of practice allows them to establish *mutual trust*. On the one hand, technology designers acquire local knowledge that allows them to understand work practice and organisational culture [22, 45]. Technology designers, therefore, understand work practices and required functionalities. On the other hand, communities of practice acquire *trust in technology innovation*, because they understand the responsibilities of tackling technological hazards [13]. They understand subtle failure modes and, hence, accept the associated risk. Therefore, communities of practice understand their responsibilities and are willing to accept the risk associated with new technology. This is because they understand how new technology fails and the relevant mitigation actions or contingency plans (available according to local knowledge). Trust in responsibilities, then, enables social relations and mutual influences, which support the investigation of different alternative design choices [21]. The development of new technology (e.g. a shift book [20]) supporting production scheduling and monitoring highlights how trust enables processes for understanding system constraints (in terms of reliability) and arising new functionalities. Trust in responsibilities allows the engagement with technology innovation. Therefore, acquiring trust in responsibilities, shifted by co-realisation mechanisms, enables co-evolutionary processes that allow and support technology innovation into work practice.

3.2.3 Dependability Knowledge

The revision of relationships between trust, responsibility and risk questions the nature of dependability [46]—*What is dependability knowledge?* Work practices highlight how people deal with technology innovation, although organisational performances often stretch stringent dependability requirements over technology innovation. Work practices accommodate technology inefficiencies to the extent that local knowledge understands technology failures and their consequences. This stresses a revision of dependability knowledge (or epistemology of dependability) with respect to technology innovation [46].

The different experiences with co-realisation highlight contingencies between trust, responsibility and risk. Mutual trust supports the sustained cooperation between communities of practice (e.g. technology designers and users). It allows a shift in responsibilities over technology innovation. On the one hand, it is possible further to understand that work practice is complementary to technology and vice versa. Both, i.e. technology and work practice, contribute differently towards overall organisational dependability. On the other hand, it highlights hazards associated with technology innovation and failure consequences. Therefore, trust in responsibilities makes, to a certain extent, technological risk acceptable.

Responsibilities, as social relationships, mediate and mitigate risk perception of technological hazards. Enabling trust allows shifting responsibilities due to technology innovation and enables co-evolutionary mechanisms of adopting and accommodating new technology into work practice. Moreover, co-evolutionary processes allow the investigation of alternative future technology solutions that may be applicable in work practices which embed past experience and localised knowledge.

3.3 Technology Trajectories

The study of *technology evolution* and *innovation* contributes to the progress of the understanding of socio-technical dynamics. On the one hand, evolution can be a source of undependabilities. On the other hand, failures may be due to technology rigidity that inhibits evolution. Evolution, therefore, represents a phenomenon in any technology and is a hazard for it. Unfortunately, technology evolution has received patchy attention in research and practice. Most engineering methodologies address change management by advocating and taking a process viewpoint. Technology driven methodologies often rely on strict configuration management policies, although they may inhibit technological evolution. On the contrary, it is possible to characterise, identify, analyse and understand technology evolution. Evolution provides a convenient socio-technical viewpoint for looking at technology. It allows, if properly understood and managed, the mitigation of technical failures [33, 47].

Unfortunately, current methodologies provide limited support with respect to the evolution of technology. Technology evolution is then a desirable feature. Technology is open, as opposed to closed, with respect to its surroundings. It captures emerging social needs. In order to understand technology, it is important to understand the role of the environment(s) in which technology is developed and deployed. The interactions in technology domains highlight the Social Shaping of Technology [30]. This comprehensive understanding allows us to characterise technology. It captures basic mechanisms of evolution, hence, technology evolution and innovation.

What is the difference between technology evolution and innovation? Taking a holistic viewpoint allows us to explain and interpret a relationship between them. Technology innovation usually involves various evolutions, among which one is technology evolution. Moreover, they relate to each other by other types of evolution. For instance, technology evolution often requires local adaptations of work practices. The hazard is that technology evolution affects local work practices. On the other hand, work practices, therefore, communities of practice, acquire new technology, or evolve one, in order to benefit from and enable technology innovation.

Although technology evolution exposes communities of practice to failures of technology innovation, it is artificial to separate these socio-technical aspects (e.g. evolution, innovation, work practice). However, narrowing the scope of the analysis allows us to understand and investigate them appropriately in order to highlight subtle relationships that characterise technology evolution and innovation.

Technology evolution and innovation are usually associated with growth of engineering knowledge [44]. This growth often results in what it seems the "normal" evolution *of technology* [31, 32]. From an engineering perspective, therefore, it is possible to characterise technology evolution and innovation in terms of technology trajectories, although technology evolution often increases the risk of failures. Thus, technology trajectories are to some extent a representation of the growth of engineering knowledge. The characterisation of technology innovation as co-evolutionary between technological artefacts and social processes also captures discontinuous engineering knowledge as "reverse salient" [24, 31, 32]. The notion of *reverse salient* [24] is fundamental in understanding and interpreting the *social processes of technological changes* [31]:

> A reverse salient is something that holds up the growth of a system [...]. System builders typically focus inventive effort [...] on the elimination of such reverse salients; they identify critical problems whose solution will eliminate them.

Social and historical accounts of technology stress the social influences on technology, namely, the social shaping of technology [30]. Although the theories underlying the social shaping of technology highlight the complexity of technological evolution and discharge the existence of obvious and predictable technological trajectories, it is still possible to identify and analyse (system) features emerging as technology trajectories. These may unveil little information about future trajectories, but they may clarify where current technology is derived from and whether or not it fits current environmental configurations (e.g. work practices). Post-analyses of technology trajectories also help in pinpointing the causes that have contributed to local (knowledge) deviations, or disruptions, as well as technology failures.

Technology trajectories highlight relationships and contingencies between technology evolution, work practice and organisational knowledge. The following sections present observational studies drawn from engineering software systems. The analysis allows us to present an engineering viewpoint and to relate it to socio-technical aspects of technology evolution and innovation. The investigations of industrial case studies allow us to acquire domain knowledge drawn from system engineering practices. This is to take a realistic account of technology evolution. Case studies drawn from industry highlight critical domain knowledge, which characterises and distinguishes industrial contexts. Finally, the identification of a broad spectrum of evolutions in socio-technical systems points out strong contingencies between technology evolution and dependability—we argue that *the better our understanding of socio-technical evolution, the better system dependability* [15, 19].

3.3.1 Requirements Evolution

Requirements evolution is an emerging phenomenon of any software related project [15]. The cost and risk associated with requirements changes inevitably increase with the progress of software projects. Requirements changes can prevent projects from ending successfully. They can also affect the main system functionalities by giving rise to uncertainties of critical system features (e.g. dependability, safety, reliability, security). These issues motivate the steadily growing interest in the requirements engineering community. Any software production involves diverse stakeholders (or communities of practice), who interact with each other by means of development deliverables (e.g. requirements specification, system design, software code), processes (e.g. change management, software development) and activities (e.g. requirements elicitation, software testing). Effective cooperation needs stakeholders to understand their different requirements viewpoints on software projects. On the one hand, requirements viewpoints relate to different system perspectives (usually associated with different stakeholders). On the other hand, requirements viewpoints support the focused analysis of system requirements. Unfortunately, poor coordination and understanding of requirements viewpoints inhibit the elicitation of requirements and affect requirements consistency. Software systems are therefore the result of engineering technical solutions through stakeholder interactions. These interactions influence how stakeholders acquire their knowledge as well as system design [44]. The way interactions capture and shape stakeholder knowledge and system design manifests over software projects as requirements changes, hence requirements evolution. Stakeholder interactions, cooperations and negotiations result in shifts in the grounds for agreement. These shifts drive requirements evolution.

The problem is how to model requirements evolution in order to capture stakeholder interactions through requirements. Although understanding stakeholder interactions highlights requirements evolution, poor understanding of the mechanisms of requirements evolution affects stakeholder interactions. This often results in poor requirements baselines that affect software production as well as system features. Modelling methodologies and languages advocate different design strategies. These strategies support different aspects of software development, although they have origins from a common *systems approach* [24] to solving complex problems and managing complex systems. In spite of common grounds, modelling methodologies and languages usually differ in the way they interpret the relationships among heterogeneous system parts (e.g. hardware components, software components, organisational components). Looking at requirements from a *heterogeneous engineering* [31, 32] perspective further explains the complex interaction between system (specification) and environment. This heterogeneous account of requirements is convenient to capture requirements evolution. The most common understanding in requirements engineering considers requirements as goals to be discovered and (design) solutions as separate technical elements. Hence, requirements engineering is reduced to be an activity where technical solutions are documented for given goals or problems. Differently, according to heterogeneous engineering, requirements specify mappings between problems and solutions. These mappings are socially constructed and negotiated through technology trajectories, i.e. sequences of mappings between solutions and problems. This view identifies evolutionary cycles of iterations of solutions searching for problems [31, 32]. This implies that requirements engineering processes consist of solutions searching for problems, rather than the other way around (that is, problems searching for solutions). Requirements evolution, as technology trajectory, therefore captures, that is, results from, the social shaping of technology [30].

3.3.2 Structuring Evolution

The analysis of evolutionary structures (e.g. architecture, traceability, coupling, dependency) provides insights and evidences of technology trajectories [3, 4, 15]. On the one hand, evolution may affect structures. On the other hand, structures may support evolution too. Modelling (requirements) evolution captures how (design) structures evolve due to stakeholder interaction. Heterogeneous engineering provides a comprehensive account of system requirements. Heterogeneous engineering stresses a holistic viewpoint that allows us to understand the underlying mechanisms of evolution of socio-technical systems. Requirements, as mappings between socio-technical solutions and problems, represent an account of the history of socio-technical issues arising and being solved within industrial settings. The formal extension of a heterogeneous account of requirements provides a framework to model and capture requirements evolution [15].

The empirical analysis of a case study drawn from the avionics domain provides an example of requirements evolution as technology trajectory [3, 4, 15]. The initial investigation looked at simple requirements trends, which were extrapolated from a data repository of requirements changes. It was possible to monitor requirements changes, because each requirement change was uniquely identified in the data repository. Furthermore, the configuration management policy within the project required uniquely identification of the releases of the software requirements specification (SRS) as well as the software code. This enabled traceability practice. The data repository consisted of the allocation of specific requirements changes to specific releases of the SRS.

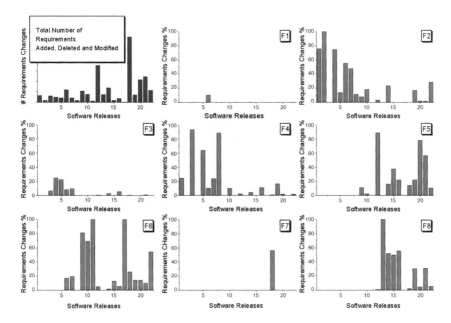

Fig. 3.2 Requirements evolution from a functional viewpoint

A functional perspective clearly pointed out that functions changed differently. Some functions were more volatile than others; of course conversely some were more stable than others. Figure 3.2 shows the number of requirements changes, i.e. Added, Deleted and Modified Requirements, over the software releases for each system function, i.e. F1–F8, forming the whole software requirements specification. Note that the classification of requirements changes (as Added, Deleted and Modified) capture the work practice within the organisation developing the software system.

There are 22 successive releases of the SRS, each one corresponding to a software release. The picture in the top-left corner of Fig. 3.2 shows the total number of changes for the whole requirements specification. All the other pictures show the percentage of requirements changes occurring in the corresponding release for each function. For instance, the function F1 changes very little in one of the early releases. F1 therefore is a stable part of the software requirements. The stability of F1 is interesting, because the specific function describes the hardware architecture of the system onto which the software architecture is mapped. Hence, the software architecture of the system is stable.

The allocation of requirements changes reflects the negotiation processes between the involved business stakeholders. This emphasises how monitoring requirements evolution relates to communities of practice, that is, stakeholder interaction and work practice. The adopted classification, on the one hand, enables organisational memory [11], on the other hand, causes *organisational forgetting*. Communities of practice (as well as organisations) adopt classifications and standards to "selectively forget things about the past in the process of producing knowledge" [11]. Two major kinds of organisational forgetting are described [11]: Clearance—"the erection of a barrier in the past at a certain point so that no information or knowledge can leak through to the present", and Erasure—"the ongoing destruction of selective traces in the present". The problem then is to understand how evolutionary system features (e.g. stable or volatile requirements) emerging as technology trajectories relate to engineering knowledge, processes and communities of practices. In practice, it is necessary to understand to what extent requirements evolution as technology trajectory captures engineering processes engaging communities of practices. The analysis of technology trajectories as resulting from negotiations between communities of practices enables engineering knowledge and makes it available for future projects. It is a process of organisational learning (forgetting), which uses, or benefits from, diverse artefacts [1, 2, 11].

3.3.3 Engineering Knowledge Growth

The analysis of evolutionary repositories stressed that it is possible to capture empirical trends in requirements changes. These evolutionary trends characterise specific project features as well as organisational aspects. Therefore, analysing evolutionary trends enables the capturing of processes of engineering knowledge—*How do evolutionary trends capture engineering knowledge?* Requirements changes, for instance, capture an extent of growth in engineering knowledge being negotiated by communities of practices.

Empirical analyses in [3, 4, 15] relied on quantitative measures of requirements changes. The behavioural analysis (or performance) of a *Requirements Maturity Index* (*RMI*) on a case study drawn from the avionics domain points out some limitations in capturing quantitatively the history of requirements changes. It is difficult to take into account evolutionary information about changes. This is because the focus of analysis captures stepwise (release-by-release) changes. Further evolutionary historical information may be obtained by answering specific questions—*How long have changes been introduced? How many releases were there without changes? How many changes have occurred since the first release?* Most of this information can be obtained by indirect measurements of requirements features. The simplest historical information consists of the *Cumulative Number of Requirements Changes* (CR_C), which measures the number of changes that have occurred since the first release.

Fig. 3.3 Average number of requirements changes (AR_C)

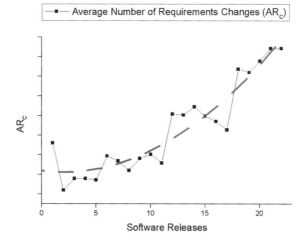

Based on the CR_C and the number of software releases, n, it is possible to define the *Average Number of Requirements Changes* (AR_C),

$$AR_C = \frac{CR_C}{n}. \tag{3.1}$$

The CR_C and the AR_C refines the RMI in *Requirements Stability Index* (*RSI*) and *Historical Requirements Maturity Index* (*HRMI*), respectively [4, 15].

Figure 3.3, for instance, shows the AR_C over the software releases. An increasing average number of requirements changes over subsequent software releases is a manifestation of growth in engineering knowledge and interactions among stakeholders. The increasing trend of AR_C characterises the case study. This is probably because many requirements were unclear or roughly defined at the start of the project. Feedback from design, implementation and (integration) testing provides further information to refine the requirements. Other case studies may manifest different distributions. Any distribution depends on various socio-technical aspects (e.g. stakeholder interaction, specified system, design process, change management policy, system life cycle).

Engineering practices need, therefore, to familiarise and naturalise organisational artefacts, such as evolutionary data repositories. There are various critical aspects that affect data collections under evolutionary scenarios—building a data repository of evolutionary data is a difficult task. The collection of data needs to be well integrated into work practices. That is, adopted organisational artefacts (e.g. classifications) need to capture and reflect work practices by clearly identifying and allocating responsibilities that respect organisational boundaries (e.g. divisions of labour). Poorly integrated data collection will result in increased workload and frustration for people who are supposed to collect data. Moreover, people will drop any data collection activity under the pressure of organisational targets or forthcoming deadlines. Moreover, communities of practice, or divisions of labour, may develop mistrust. This will result in *out-of-date* data repositories. Substantial effort will then be required in order to update these repositories during the final stages of the development process. In the worst case the repositories will become unusable and ineffective. They will, moreover, fail to provide any evolutionary feedback in the development process. The data organisation is another aspect concerning an effective collection of evolutionary information. Data organisation affects our ability to analyse and identify evolutionary features. Unsuitable organisation will provide limited support to identify any emergent information. Data organisations should fulfil specific goals and address specific issues. For instance, assume that a simple history of changes is the main record of requirements changes. The history of requirements changes easily provides evidence of tracking changes for certification purpose. Unfortunately, it provides limited feedback to the organisation. This is because it lacks any support to identify evolutionary relationships. The measurement of requirements evolution requires a well-defined standard policy to classify requirements changes. Even a simple classification of requirements changes implies specific work practices, policies and responsibilities.

3.3.4 Evolutionary Dependencies

Requirements management methodologies and practices rely on *requirements traceability* information. Traceability practice requires that an organisation recognises the importance of requirements. Traceability is crucial for requirements management, although it is realistically difficult to decide which information should be maintained. Traceability matrices or tables maintain relevant requirements information. Requirements are entries matched with other elements in these representations (e.g. row or column entries). Traceability representations often assume that requirements are uniquely identified. Moreover, it has to establish well-defined policies to collect and maintain requirements. Unfortunately, traceability provides limited support for requirements management. There are various limitations (e.g. scalability, evolution and timeliness) that affect traceability practice. However, requirements traceability provides useful information about requirements, although traceability manifests emergent evolutionary aspects just as requirements do. It allows us to understand important requirements dependencies, which constrain software production—*What are (requirements) dependencies?* Requirements dependencies, as an instance of traceability, identify relationships between requirements. Dependencies, like requirements changes, represent an extent of emerging constraints due to the social shaping of technology. They constrain requirements evolution. It is important to capture these dependencies in order to further understand requirements evolution.

The application of a (logical) framework[3] provides further evidence that it is possible to capture and model evolutionary information about requirements [15, 19]. This allows us to understand emerging properties of complex systems [26]. Evolutionary dependencies take into account (that is, extend requirements traceability) that requirements change over consecutive releases. They stress how changes propagate through emergent, direct or indirect (e.g. testing results, implementation constraints), requirements dependencies. Evolutionary dependencies, therefore, capture the fact that if changes affect some requirements, they may affect other requirements eventually. That is, they account for how changes will manifest into requirements. Evolutionary dependencies, therefore, take into account how requirements changes affect other requirements. Change rationale can trigger subsequent requirements changes. Requirements responses to change rationale refine evolutionary dependencies. That is, the way changes spread over requirements represents a classification of evolutionary dependencies [15, 19].

It is possible to identify two general types of changes, hence types of evolutionary dependencies: *single release* and *multiple release*. Single release changes affect a single requirements release, whereas multiple release changes affect subsequent requirement releases. This is because changes require further refinements or information. It is possible to further refine these two types as single or multiple requirements. It depends on whether requirements changes affect single or multiple (type of) requirements. This assumes that requirements group together homogeneously (e.g. functional requirements, subsystem requirements, component requirements). The most complex evolutionary dependencies occur as requirements changes affect multiple requirements over subsequent releases. In this case, it is possible to have circular cascade effects. Requirements changes feedback (or refine) requirements through (circular) requirements dependencies. Complex dependencies, therefore, consist of combinations (or compositions) of the basic ones, i.e. cascade, self-loop and refinement-loop dependencies. Note that the dependency classification reflects work practices observed by the empirical investigations of requirements changes.

---

[3] It is necessary to enrich the semantics interpretation of the accessibility relation, i.e. dependency, between functional requirements by associating weights with each pair of related *possible worlds*, i.e. functional requirements. Intuitively, technical solutions (matching requirements) are *accessible possibilities* or *possible worlds* in solution spaces available in the production environment. A solution space, therefore, is just a collection of solutions, which represent the organisational engineering knowledge [44] resulting from the social shaping of technology [30]. The definition in [15] intentionally recalls the notion of possible worlds underlying *Kripke models*. Thus, solutions are Kripke models, whereas problems are formulas of (propositional) modal logic. Collections of problems (i.e. problem spaces) are suspected issues arising during system production. Kripke models (i.e. solutions) provide the semantics in order to interpret the validity of (propositional) modalities (i.e. problems). *Propositional Modal Logic* allows us to express *modalities*. Formulas of propositional modal logic capture system properties like *safety* and *liveness*. For instance, let us consider the formula $\Box P \to P$. The formula means that if a property P is valid at every accessible possible world, then it is actually valid at the real world. It represents a simple safety property that states 'nothing bad ever happens'. Another example is the formula $\Box P \to \Diamond P$. The formula means that if the property P is valid at every accessible possible world, then it will be valid eventually. It represents a simple liveness property that states 'something good eventually happens'.

Fig. 3.4 A weighted model
of evolutionary dependencies

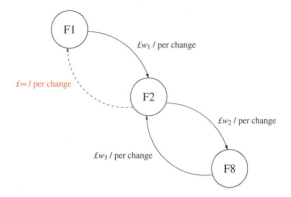

A (logical) framework allows us to capture evolutionary requirements dependencies as transformation of technical solutions being available in a specific domain. Examples drawn from an avionics case study [3, 4, 15] provide a realistic account of requirements dependencies. The examples show how the heterogeneous framework captures evolutionary features of requirements, hence requirements evolution [15, 19]. Evolutionary dependencies, therefore, are examples of growing engineering knowledge, that is, evolutionary dependencies are instances of emergent technology trajectories of complex systems. The underlying assumption is that design decisions influencing (requirements) changes are the results of negotiations among stakeholders, not merely technical decisions. Modelling dependencies, for example, allow us to refine cost-benefit analysis of requirements changes. It is possible to associate a cost for each dependency relationship between (functional) requirements.

It is possible to calculate the cost of propagating changes by summing the weights for all relationships between functions involved in particular requirements changes. Moreover, information about requirements evolution and volatility would allow the adjustment of cost models. This information would enable the cost-effective management of requirements changes and the risk associated with them. However, the absence of a relationship from one function to another could be interpreted as having a very high cost (e.g. infinite or non-affordable cost). Figure 3.4 shows an example of complex dependencies identified in the avionics case study [15, 19].

Figure 3.4 shows the evolutionary dependency model between three functional requirements (i.e. F1, F2 and F8). It is possible to extend the model by labelling each transaction with the cost associated with each triggered requirements change. Thus, it is possible to calculate the cost of any change in F1 that triggers changes in F2 and F8 eventually. The cost of cascading changes is w_1, w_2 and w_3 for changes propagating from F1 to F2, from F2 to F8 and from F8 to F2, respectively. Therefore, if requirements exhibit the specific evolutionary dependency model (empirically constructed), the cost of implementing the associated changes would be $n(w_1 + i(w2 + w3))$ (where n is the number of changes in F1 that trigger changes in F2 and F8 eventually, and i is the number of times that changes are reiterated or negotiated between F2 and F8). Whereas, the accessibility from F2 to F1 (represented by a dashed arrow) would be very expensive, because it requires changing the requirements of the software architecture (i.e. F1). Although changes in F2 could affect F1, it is undesirable due to high cost and risk associated with changing F1. The formal framework models emergent evolutionary dependencies. It captures how evolutionary dependencies change through subsequent transformations.

The idea is that models of dependencies are refined through subsequent dependencies, hence evolutionary dependencies whereas *anomalies* (modelled as propositional modal formulas) highlight dependency inconsistencies due to requirements changes. Subsequent modelling transformation therefore solves problems (i.e. dependency inconsistencies) that arise in proposed evolutionary dependencies. Hence, a sequence of dependency transformations captures emergent requirements dependencies. That is, it is possible to construct models of requirements dependencies using dependency transformations. The evolutionary dependency models allow the gathering of engineering knowledge. On the one hand, the models capture the history of socio-technical issues arising and being solved within industrial settings. On the other hand, it is possible to infer engineering knowledge from the evolutionary dependency models.

3.4 Judging Moving Targets

The characterisation of technology innovation highlights a trend of growth of engineering knowledge [44]. Epistemologic accounts of engineering activities contribute to diverse types of knowledge [44]. Social studies highlight the role of computer systems to the formation of (inductive) knowledge [29]. This highlights contingencies between trust, risk and knowledge. These contingencies are crucial in the presence of 'unforeseen' emergent behaviours of complex systems [25]. Historical accounts of the evolution of technology characterise emergent behaviours as *technology trajectories*, or *normal evolution of technology* [31, 32]. These trajectories capture various design decisions or technology solutions taken at some point in the development of technological systems. Design decisions—considering the systemic view of technology [24]—may often employ COTS systems. The problem then is how to assess such systems, that is, how to construct supporting arguments. For instance, the certification of safety-critical systems often involves—due to compliance with industry standards—the development of *safety cases* [43]. A safety case articulates a (structured) safety argumentation, or judgement, of the system under scrutiny. Moreover, emergent system behaviour often requires change or revision of initial arguments, e.g. due to failures or knowledge arising.

3.4.1 Constructing Arguments

Decomposing (software) systems to small and manageable entities is essential in order to support system design process phases effectively, from design to certification. Nowadays, there is an increasing number of systems that consist of COTS software.

This aims to increase software reusability across industrial contexts as well as to reduce software cost. The financial pressure on technology innovation often requires the adoption of COTS systems. In the long term, it is believed that COTS software may increase the overall system dependability. An increasing business demand for 'cheaper' and 'more dependable' software has supported the popularity of COTS software. Thus, system dependability often relies on (outsourcing) COTS software. New issues arise in the certification of COTS software that relies on the trustworthiness of third parties. The problem then is to collect evidence that supports the use of COTS software in safety-related systems—*Is it possible to sensibly justify the use of COTS components for safety-critical domains? Is there any knowledge useful for the construction of supporting arguments?*

The assessment of such systems requires further attention in order to identify potential hazards for their deployment in safety-critical domains [6–8]. Technology may behave safely for a long period of time, however, individual (software) components may exhibit emergent properties when analysed in a different context. Although they may exhibit extensive safe usages, they need additional insurance before being justifiably adopted in safety-critical domains [6, 7]. The *Software Criticality Analysis* (SCA) in [6, 7] assesses the extent to which each component contributes to the safety of the whole system and highlights contingencies between system usages and safety insurance. The SCA methodology furthermore points out "segregation between software components with different safety importance" [6, 7].

The SCA methodology consists of a combination of hazard and operability analysis, i.e. HAZOP,[4] based on design documents and software inspections [6, 7]. The results point out that the assessment based only on architecture and design documents would have been misleading. The SCA methodology helps to focus safety assurance activities on specific critical components.

The benefit is two-fold. First, it identifies safety-critical components. Second, the increased focus on critical components supports cost-reduction over subsequent validation activities (e.g. software reviews, testing, static analysis and empirical studies). Reengineering activities, moreover, provide an independent validation of design documents and system structures. Although architectural and design considerations provide limited support in order to assess criticalities of COTS systems, the SCA methodology allows the identification of critical components as well as the tailoring of validation methodologies and activities to these components [6, 7]. Therefore, the adoption of COTS systems in safety-critical domains requires a supportive safety argument. The construction of such arguments requires a combination of different

---

[4] *Hazard and Operability Analysis* (HAZOP) [26, 43] involves "identifying the interconnections between components within the system and determining the corresponding interactions" [43]. Component interactions identify flows, referred as "entities" having certain properties or "attributes", which define the system's operation. Any deviation from these properties (i.e. attributes) highlights concerns with respect to the system's operation [26, 43].

methodologies tackling specific classes of faults (e.g. unsafe language constructs or covert flows) [8]. The different methodologies support diverse arguments increasing our confidence in the safety arguments and system behaviour.

> Software reliability presents other contingencies in the construction of supportive arguments [38, 39]. For instance, results in software engineering point out issues with independence claims over design diversity [27]. Software evolution, although it may exhibit increasing trends of reliability, may reduce diversity over multi-version software [39]. Other contingencies may be related to the intrinsic complexity of assessing systems employing COTS components as a strategy for technology evolution [38]. These contingencies require us to judge the technology according to diverse arguments supporting dependability claims or safety cases. Although diverse arguments, intuitively, should increase our *confidence* in dependability claims, the compositionality of diverse arguments hides contingencies too [9, 10, 28].

Figure 3.5 , for instance, shows a multi-legged argument combining two evidences (i.e. *A* and *B*) in order to support a claim (i.e. assertion *G*) [9, 10]. The two evidences could support a probabilist argument over testing results and a formal argument over program correctness, respectively. A probabilistic argument, based on statistical data, over reliability may support quantitative assessments, although it may invalidate a fault-free argument over formally-proved correctness. The resulting *conflicting*, or counter, arguments affect our confidence over the constructed (e.g. compositionality into a two-leg argument) argumentation (e.g. one of the claims is false), supporting knowledge (e.g. the proof is wrong), hence, overall system judgement. The analytical (probabilistic) account of multi-legged arguments highlights subtle contingencies in the dependencies underlying the arguments' assumptions [28]. In particular, there exists counterexamples in which the combination of two arguments may decrease our overall confidence (in terms of "probability that the claim is true") in the main claim. Although there is evidence supporting an argument, the same evidence invalidates the other argument (of diverse nature) in a multi-legged one or decreases our confidence in the structured argumentation [28].

3.4.2 Reusing Arguments

Hazard and safety analyses for safety-critical systems are major activities in order to assess whether the risk associated with any specific design is acceptable [26, 43]. However, they require sufficient coverage and rigour to provide enough evidence that the proposed solutions mitigate the identified risk. This often implies exhaustive hazard and safety analyses, although these are time consuming and error prone. Reuse is a strategy to reduce the cost of developing hazard and safety analyses. The analysis and understanding of technology trajectories and the knowledge they carry

Fig. 3.5 A structured
multi-legged argument

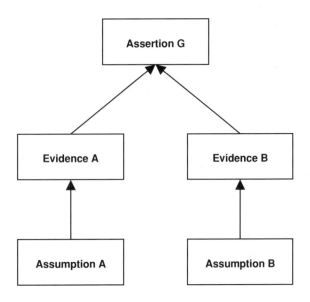

may support reuse strategies in order to optimise the cost of collecting supporting evidences or engineering knowledge [40, 41]. Unfortunately, reuse strategies may affect the effectiveness, correctness and validity of hazard and safety analyses. It is possible to identify the extent of reuse in hazard analysis [40, 41]. The methodology in [40, 41] relies on an edit distance algorithm that highlights argument clusters and investigates hazard analysis reuse in two case studies. Both case studies uncover a considerable amount of reuse. The first case study highlights reuse in the construction of safety arguments. The analysis identifies the argument structures in the hazard analysis. Therefore, it is possible to assess the amount of reuse. If reuse is substantial, it can give a misleading impression of rigorous coverage. This is obviously undesirable for the dependability analysis of safety-critical systems. However, the amount of reuse provides limited indication of the validity of safety cases. In order to support the construction of safety arguments, the analysis needs to determine whether or not there exist suitable reusable arguments in the current context.

The second study in [40, 41] is concerned with reuse changes resulting from tool support. Although tool support enables the customisation of reused arguments, most of them are customised trivially. The edit distance algorithm allows the identification and the enumeration of reused safety arguments. This enhances our ability to gather knowledge and make it available within application domains for reuse.

3.4.3 Changing Arguments

Conventional safety analyses are deemed acceptable in some industry domains (e.g. nuclear or chemical), which present well-confined entities (e.g. industrial plants) with limited predictable interactions with their surroundings. In such cases, design stresses the separation of safety-related components (or system parts) from others. This forces and ensures the independence of failures. Therefore, in these application domains, it is possible to identify acceptable trade-offs between completeness and manageability of safety arguments during the definition and identification of the system under analysis. However, the evolutionary nature of engineering knowledge requires us to understand how to collect knowledge about technology and what type of knowledge. Moreover, emergent behaviour [25] emphasises the necessity of adopting evolutionary methodologies when revising engineering knowledge about evolving technology systems, that is, analysing technology trajectories. This highlights the evolutionary nature of assessing and judging dependability claims of evolving technology [16–18].

The ATM domain, for instance, highlights how safety-critical activities rely on complex socio-technical interactions. Interactions are means for enabling the (re)distribution of knowledge among heterogeneous actors and resources. The distribution of knowledge and its interaction strategies allow the characterisation of socio-technical interactions. These *complex interactions* expose the limitations of safety analysis. ATM systems operate in open and dynamic environments for which it is difficult to identify *complex interactions* [17]. In particular, there is a complex interaction between aircraft's controls and ATM safety functions. Unfortunately, this complex interaction may give rise to catastrophic failures. Hence, failure separation (i.e. understanding the mechanisms to enhance failure independence) would increase the overall ATM safety. Critical decisions are still demanded of people whose behaviour is less predictable than that of automated systems. On the one hand, people (e.g. air traffic controllers and pilots) using codified languages and procedures mediate complex interactions. On the other hand, technology mediates people interaction too. It is necessary further to understand how people use external artefacts (e.g. tools) in order to mediate these interactions. Moreover, capturing emergent behaviour will enhance our understanding of how people adopt technological artefacts and adapt their behaviour in order to accommodate technological evolution, technology innovation. Unfortunately, the evolution of technological systems often corresponds to a lack of trust affecting work practice. Work practice and systems evolve in response to demand and a culture of continuous improvements. A comprehensive, that is, holistic, account of systems will support modelling the mechanisms of evolution. This will enhance strategies for deploying new system configurations or major system upgrades. On the one hand, modelling and understanding system evolution support the engineering of evolving systems. On the other hand, modelling and understanding system evolution allow the communication of changes across organisational boundaries and divisions of labour. This would enhance visibility of

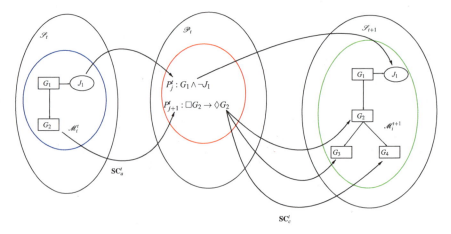

Fig. 3.6 An example of safety case changes

system evolution as well as trust in transition to operations, or generally speaking, adoption of technology innovation.

Failures of safety-critical systems, unfortunately, highlight safety issues related to system evolution and emergent complex interactions. It is often the case that diverse causes interacted and triggered particular unsafe conditions. Although safety analysis (e.g. a safety case) argues system safety, complex interactions giving rise to failures expose the limitations of (structured) safety arguments. Therefore, it is necessary to take changes into account in safety arguments [16, 18]. It is possible to use a logical framework—similar to the one capturing evolutionary dependencies—for modelling safety case evolution [15, 16, 18]. The framework extends the use of evolutionary modelling in [15] to safety case evolution [16–18]. Modelling safety case changes relies on a formal extension of evolutionary modelling. The underlying idea is to provide a formal representation of safety cases and issues arising. On the one hand, the formalisation of safety cases and problems supports model-driven judgement. On the other hand, it allows us to capture safety case evolution formally. Figure 3.6, for instance, shows a transformation that captures (structured) safety case changes [15, 17]. The safety case transformation captures the changes from the initial safety case (i.e. $\mathcal{M}_i^t$) to the revised safety case (i.e. $\mathcal{M}_i^{t+1}$). An accident, or emerging knowledge, invalidates the justification J_1. The satisfaction of the subgoal G_2 is insufficient for the satisfaction of the goal G_1. This highlights some safety problems (i.e. P_j^t and P_{j+1}^t).

The safety case transformation addresses the highlighted problems into the proposed safety case. In order to address the highlighted problems, it is necessary to change the initial safety case. The proposed changes are taken into account in the proposed safety case. Note that there might be different proposed safety cases addressing the selected safety problems. The transformation identifies the safety case construction and judgement in terms of safety arguments and constraints. The safety case evolution consists of the collections of mappings between safety cases and emergent problems. The first part of a safety case consists of the safety arguments, which capture the relationship that comes from safety cases looking for problems. The second part of a safety case consists of the safety constraints, which capture how future safety cases address given problems. These definitions enable us further to interpret and understand safety case changes, hence safety case evolution. Therefore, the framework enables the implementation of an evolutionary safety analysis [16–18]. The modelling of safety case evolution provides new insights on safety case judgements and safety analysis. First, the framework captures how safety cases evolve in order to accommodate arising safety problems. Subsequent safety cases identify the construction and judgement in terms of safety arguments and constraints. Second, the framework supports industry guidelines and best practices, which emphasise the iterative nature of safety analysis [16]. The framework supports safety judgement as well as evolutionary safety analysis [16–18]. The underlying evolutionary aspects characterise work practice in the safety analysis of continuously evolving industry domains (e.g. ATM). Finally, the framework relies on basic logic models (i.e. Kripke models) that enable reasoning about knowledge and uncertainty. This highlights safety judgement (in particular, the construction of safety cases) as an organisational process. That is, the safety judgement consists of gathering organisational knowledge about the system. This further highlights how organisational (knowledge) failures affect safety.

3.5 Evolutionary Hazards

The evolutionary nature of technology highlights three different classes of *evolutionary hazards*: *evolving work practices*, *understanding technology trajectories* and *judging moving targets*. The different case studies point out the coupling between technology and work practice. In particular, work practice and technology co-evolve. On the one hand, technology evolution is driven to some extent by technological innovations. On the other hand, technology innovation is often characterised by social groupings engaging technological as well as political arguments. This emphasises the criticality of technology within organisational information infrastructures to maintaining and supporting alignment between organisational structures (e.g. in terms of divisions of labour) and objectives (e.g. strategic business targets). Failing to understand the coupling between technology and work practice poses a risk to technology evolution.

A lack of understanding of the subtle relationships between technology and work practice creates mistrust in technology innovation. Moreover, mechanisms of technological evolution concern divisions of labour, which may exploit, intentionally or accidentally, technology innovation to alter organisational boundaries, e.g. by shifting responsibilities. It is also important to understand how technology innovation (by embedding knowledge into boundary objects or infrastructures) supports formal as well as informal organisational knowledge supporting communities of practice. Failing to address evolving work practices exposes organisations to evolutionary hazards and inhibits opportunities for redundancy and diversity to strengthen organisational resilience to complex interaction failures.

Technology trajectories emerge as a result of evolutionary negotiations involving communities of practice. These negotiations, although involving technical arguments to some extent, involve design decisions as well as social struggles. However, technology innovation consists of cycles of discoveries and exploitations. Further understanding these underlying cycles and mechanisms of technology evolution enhances our ability to manage and configure technology innovation. This highlights how the complexity of technology resides in subtle interactions of evolution taking into account emergent organisational (e.g. social) relationships.

Socio-technical relationships extend technology complexity and innovation. This requires us to understand, on the one hand, drivers of technology evolution, as well as, on the other hand, emergent engineering knowledge registering any socio-technical shifts. These shifts expose the limitations of assessing technology innovation. Moreover, they inhibit our ability to advocate and argue technology innovation. Capturing these complex interactions enhances our ability to construct, reuse and change technology arguments (e.g. safety arguments). This requires us to unveil the complexity underlying technology. Understanding mechanisms of interaction and evolution intends to some extent to mitigate *unforeseen* dependencies. This makes the problem of assessing technology innovation theoretically difficult and complex (e.g. reliability assessment of COTS upgrades). System failures or emergent knowledge may often invalidate our assumptions. They require the re-negotiation of structured technology arguments (e.g. multi-legged arguments). Moreover, underlying evolutionary processes require us to adapt engineering knowledge and the construction of supporting (e.g. dependability) arguments for technology innovation.

Table 3.1 summarises emergent evolutionary hazards associated with technology and its innovation. Technology evolution, therefore, highlights contingencies in innovation. It questions the nature of mechanisms underlying evolution. In particular, it highlights contingencies between emerging technological risk, trust in technology and engineering knowledge. Technology evolution questions our understanding of innovation and its risk: *What hazards does technology innovation involve? What is the risk of technology innovation? How are we to trust technology innovation?* Innovation requires technology to be adapted to emergent and negotiated knowledge.

3.5.1 Addressing Evolutionary Hazards

Evolutionary hazards expose organisations to failures as well as change resistances inhibiting technology innovation. Safety analyses adapt and reuse system design models (often produced by third parties). Technical, organisational and cost-related reasons often determine this choice, although design models are unfit for safety analysis. Design models provide limited support to safety analysis, because they are tailored for system designers. Moreover, they provide limited support for technology evolution. The definition of an adequate model and of an underlying methodology for

Table 3.1 Evolutionary hazards

Hazard	Description
Technology and work practice co-evolution	Technology innovation involves evolving work practice. Lack of alignment between technology and work practice may expose organisations to evolutionary failures
Shift in responsibility	The introduction of technology may shift responsibilities across organisational boundaries and divisions of labour
Evolutionary engineering knowledge	Technology trajectories characterise innovation. They represent an account of how engineering and negotiation processes capture emergent engineering knowledge
Constructing, reusing and changing supporting arguments	System failures and emergent knowledge may invalidate structured arguments and inhibit our ability to reuse them. A lack of understanding of subsequent arguments may affect our ability to judge and assess system dependability. Contingencies in evolving dependability arguments expose organisations to system failures

its construction will be highly beneficial for performing evolutionary safety analysis supporting technology evolution. Currently, the model definition phase cannot be properly addressed as an integral part of safety analysis, mostly due to limited costs and resources. However, it is possible to understand and capture basic evolutionary mechanisms. In particular, it is possible to analyse the relationships between technology innovation and work practice. Moreover, it is possible to capture how these relationships shape technology trajectories. An evolutionary account emerging from empirical studies highlights three main points in order to support evolutionary processes (e.g. evolutionary safety analysis) and to capture emerging complex interactions effectively.

First, the resulting evolutionary account questions the system boundaries and the required level of modelling detail. These aspects vary considerably from design models to risk analysis models, since system parts that need to be specified in details for the design may be much less relevant than information required from a safety analysis point of view. The typical drawback experienced in most cases is that resources for risk analysis may be consumed in investigating detailed aspects of every system part, instead of trying to identify unknown hazards that may be related to elements not central in the design model. Furthermore, it is often the case that system boundaries can be neatly defined with respect to the design objectives, whilst risk analysis often requires the adoption of a wide focus. For instance, most recent major incidents occurred in the civil aviation domain proved to stem from unexpected interactions from a large variety of elements, differently located in space and time. The investigation report of an accident between two aircraft highlights that although individual ATM systems and procedures work properly, the complex socio-technical interactions may, unfortunately, result in a catastrophic event [17]. Those elements were often judged as outside of the system boundaries (or outside of normal operating conditions) when safety analysis has been conducted. An evolutionary account of technology allows the gathering of emergent knowledge. In particular, it is necessary to capture how safety cases evolve in order to address safety problems arising. Subsequent structured safety arguments identify the safety case construction and judgement in terms of safety argumentations and constraints. Emerging safety cases consist of collections of mappings between safety cases and problems arising. Addressing these relationships corresponds to arguing safety for evolving technology. The identification of emergent knowledge enables us further to interpret and understand technology evolution, hence technology innovation. This, therefore, would support the implementation of evolutionary safety analysis.

The second point directly addresses unexpected complex interactions between system elements as main sources of incidents. Best practices and standards in safety analysis prescribe that the mutual impact between different hazards should be analysed. A system model is a key support to perform this task effectively, but the possible interactions need to be represented explicitly. On the contrary, models defined for design purposes usually outline the relationship between system elements by a functional (or physical) decomposition. Although it is possible to exploit design models for safety analysis, the functional decomposition principle may unduly provide the structure for the analysis of incident causal dynamics, thus failing to acknowledge their different underlying nature. Furthermore, a correct model should ensure that interactions and mutual impact between different hazards are analysed. It should also outline interactions between everyday productive processes in 'normal operating conditions', since risk factors are likely to interact along these lines.

The third point is concerned with the possibility of effective re-use of (part of) supporting arguments to inform other safety analyses. A framework relying on basic logic models or structured arguments enables reasoning about knowledge and uncertainty. This highlights safety judgement (that is, the construction of safety cases) as an organisational process. That is, the safety judgement consists of gathering organisational knowledge about the system. This further highlights how organisational knowledge failures affect safety. This would ensure that part of the safety feedback and experience related to a system can be beneficial when introducing major changes to the current system or when developing new similar systems. Similarly, the effective reuse of safety arguments supports safety analyses that would achieve a good balance between exhaustiveness and cost, as findings of closely related analyses could be easily considered.

References

1. Ackerman MS, Halverson CA (2000) Reexamining organizational memory. Commun ACM 43(1):59–64. doi:10.1145/323830.323845
2. Ackerman MS, Halverson CA (2004) Organizational memory as objects, processes, and trajectories: an examination of organizational memory in use. Computer Supported Cooperative Work 13(2):155–189. doi:10.1023/B:COSU.0000045805.77534.2a
3. Anderson S, Felici M (2001) Requirements evolution—from process to product oriented management. In: Bomarius F, Komi-Sirviö S (eds) Proceedings of the third international conference on product focused software process improvement, PROFES 2001, Springer, no. 2188 in LNCS, pp 27–41. doi:10.1007/3-540-44813-6_6
4. Anderson S, Felici M (2002) Quantitative aspects of requirements evolution. In: Proceedings of the 26th annual international conference on computer software and applications conference, COMPSAC 2002, IEEE Computer Society, pp 27–32. doi:10.1109/CMPSAC.2002.1044529
5. Avižienis A, Laprie J-C, Randell B, Landwehr C (2004) Basic concepts and taxonomy of dependable and secure computing. IEEE Trans Dependable Secur Comput 1(1):11–33. doi:10.1109/TDSC.2004.2
6. Bishop P, Bloomfield R, Clement C, Guerra S (2003) Software criticality analysis of COTS/SOUP. Reliab Eng Syst Saf 81(3):291–301. doi:10.1016/S0951-8320(03)00093-0
7. Bishop P, Bloomfield R, Clement T, Guerra S (2002) Software criticality analysis of COTS/SOUP. In: Anderson S, Bologna S, Felici M (eds) Proceedings of the 21st international conference on computer safety, reliability and security, SAFECOMP 2002, Springer, no. 2434 in LNCS, pp 198–211. doi:10.1007/3-540-45732-1_20
8. Bishop P, Bloomfield R, Clement T, Guerra S, Jones C (2003) Integrity static analysis of COTS/SOUP. In: Anderson S, Felici M, Littlewood B (eds) Proceedings of the 22nd international conference on computer safety, Reliability and Security, SAFECOMP 2003, Springer, no. 2788 in LNCS, pp 63–76. doi:10.1007/978-3-540-39878-3_6
9. Bloomfield R, Littlewood B (2003) Multi-legged arguments: the impact of diversity upon confidence in dependability arguments. In: Proceedings of the 2003 international conference on dependable systems and networks, DSN'03, IEEE Computer Society, pp 25–34. doi:10.1109/DSN.2003.1209913
10. Bloomfield R, Littlewood B(2006) On the use of diverse arguments to increase confidence in dependability claims. In: Besnard D, Gacek C, Jones CB (eds) Structure for dependability: computer-based systems from an interdisciplinary perspective, Springer, Chap 13, pp 254–268. doi:10.1007/1-84628-111-3_13
11. Bowker GC, Star SL (1999) Sorting things out: classification and its consequences. The MIT Press, Cambridge
12. Bruseberg A (2006) The design of complete systems: providing human factors guidance for COTS acquisition. Reliab Eng Syst Saf 91(12):1554–1565. doi:10.1016/j.ress.2006.01.016
13. Büscher M, Shapiro D, Hartswood M, Procter R, Slack R, Voß A, Mogensen P (2002) Promises, premises and risks: sharing responsibilities, working up trust and sustaining commitment in participatory design projects. In: Binder T, Gregory J, Wagner I (eds) Proceedings of the participatory design conference, PDC 2002, pp 183–192
14. Douglas M, Wildavsky A (1982) Risk and culture: an essay on the selection of technological and environmental dangers. University of California Press, California
15. Felici M (2004) Observational models of requirements evolution. PhD thesis, School of Informatics, University of Edinburgh, Edinburgh
16. Felici M (2005) Evolutionary safety analysis: motivations from the air traffic management domain. In: Winther R, Gran BA, Dahll G (eds) Proceedings of the 24th international conference on computer safety, reliability and security, SAFECOMP 2005, Springer, no. 3688 in LNCS, pp 208–221. doi:10.1007/11563228_16
17. Felici M (2006a) Capturing emerging complex interactions: safety analysis in air traffic management. Reliab Eng Syst Saf 91(12):1482–1493. doi:10.1016/j.ress.2006.01.010

18. Felici M (2006b) Modeling safety case evolution—examples from the air traffic management domain. In: Guelfi N, Savidis A (eds) Proceedings of the 2nd international workshop on rapid integration of software engineering techniques, RISE 2005, Springer no. 3943 in LNCS, pp 81–96. doi:10.1007/11751113_7

19. Felici M (2006c) Structuring evolution: on the evolution of socio-technical systems. In: Besnard D, Gacek C, Jones C (eds) Structure for dependability: computer-based systems from an interdisciplinary perspective, chap 3, Springer, pp 49–73. doi:10.1007/1-84628-111-3_3

20. Halverson CA (2002) Activity theory and distributed cognition: or what does CSCW need to do with theories? Computer Supported Cooperative Work 11(1–2):243–267. doi:10.1023/A:1015298005381

21. Hartswood M, Procter P, Slack R, Voß A, Büscher M, Rouncefield M, Rouchy P (2002) Co-realisation: towards a principled synthesis of ethnomethodology and participatory design. Scand J Inf Syst 14(2):9–30

22. Hartswood M, Procter R, Slack R, Soutter J, VoßA, Rouncefield M (2002) The benefits of a long engagement: from contextual design to the co-realisation of work affording artefacts. In: Proceedings of NordiCHI, ACM, pp 283–286. doi:10.1145/572020.572066

23. Hollnagel E (1993) Human reliability analysis: context and control. Academic Press, London

24. Hughes, AC, Hughes, TP (eds) (2000) Systems, experts, and computers: the systems approach in management and engineering, world war II and after. The MIT Press, Cambridge

25. Johnson CW (2006) What are emergent properties and how do they affect the engineering of complex systems? Reliab Eng Syst Saf 91(12):1475–1481. doi:10.1016/j.ress.2006.01.008

26. Leveson NG (1995) SAFEWARE: system safety and computers. Addison-Wesley, London

27. Littlewood B, Popov P, Strigini L (2001) Modeling software design diversity: a review. ACM Comput Surv 33(2):177–208. doi:10.1145/384192.384195

28. Littlewood B, Wright D (2007) The use of multi-legged arguments to increase confidence in safety claims for software-based systems: a study based on a BBN analysis of an idealised example. IEEE Trans on Softw Eng 33(5):347–365. doi:10.1109/TSE.2007.1002

29. MacKenzie D (2001) Mechanizing proof: computing, risk, and trust. The MIT Press, Cambridge

30. MacKenzie, D, Wajcman, J (eds) (1999) The social shaping of technology, 2nd edn. Open University Press, Buckingham

31. MacKenzie DA (1990) Inventing accuracy: a historical sociology of nuclear missile guidance. The MIT Press, Cambridge

32. MacKenzie DA (1996) Knowing machines: essays on technical change. The MIT Press, Cambridge

33. Neumann PG (1995) Computer related risks. The ACM Press, New York

34. Norman DA (1993) Things that make us smart: defining human attributes in the age of the machine. Perseus Books, Cambridge

35. Perrow C (1999) Normal accidents: living with high-risk technologies. Princeton University Press, New Jersey

36. Petroski H (1982) To engineer is human: the role of failure in successful design. Vintage Books, New York

37. Petroski H (1994) Design paradigms: case histories of error and judgment in engineering. Cambridge University Press, Cambridge

38. Popov P (2002) Reliability assessment of legacy safety-critical systems upgraded with off-the-shelf components. In: Anderson S, Bologna S, Felici M (eds) Proceedings of the 21st international conference on computer safety, reliability and security, SAFECOMP 2002, Springer, no. 2434 in LNCS, pp 139–150, doi:10.1007/3-540-45732-1_15

39. Popov P, Littlewood B (2004) The effect of testing on reliability of fault-tolerant software. In: Proceedings of the 2004 international conference on dependable systems and networks, DSN'04, IEEE Comput Soc, pp 265–274. doi:10.1109/DSN.2004.1311896

40. Smith SP, Harrison MD (2003) Reuse in hazard analysis: identification and support. In: Anderson S, Felici M, Littlewood B (eds) Proceedings of the 22nd international conference

on computer safety, reliability and security, SAFECOMP 2003, Springer, no. 2788 in LNCS, pp 382–395. doi:10.1007/978-3-540-39878-3_30

41. Smith SP, Harrison MD (2005) Measuring reuse in hazard analysis. Reliab Eng Syst Saf 89(1):93–104. doi:10.1016/j.ress.2004.08.010

42. Sommerville I (2007) Software engineering, eighth edn. Addison-Wesley, Harlow

43. Storey N (1996) Safety-critical computer systems. Addison-Wesley, Harlow

44. Vincenti WG (1990) What engineers know and how they know it: analytical studies from aeronautical history. The Johns Hopkins University Press, Baltimore

45. Voß A, Procter R, Slack R, Hartswood M, Williams R, Rouncefield M (2002) Accomplishing 'just-in-time' production. In: Johnson C (ed) Human decision making and control, GIST technical report G2002-1, pp 209–211

46. Voß A, Slack R, Procter R, Williams R, Hartswood M, Rouncefield M (2002) Dependability as ordinary action. In: Anderson S, Bologna S, Felici M (eds) Proceedings of the 21st international conference on computer safety, reliability and security, SAFECOMP 2002, Springer, no. 2434 in LNCS, pp 32–43, doi:10.1007/3-540-45732-1_5

47. Wallace DR, Kuhn DR (1999) Lessons from 342 medical device failures. In: Proceedings of the 4th IEEE international symposium on high-assurance systems engineering, HASE, IEEE Computer Society, pp 123–131

48. Williams R, Stewart J, Slack R (2005) Social learning in technological innovation: experimenting with information and communication technologies. Edward Elgar, Cheltenham

Chapter 4
Social Connectivity

Social accounts of technological artefacts and their adoptions by communities of practice highlight the mechanisms of shaping technology. On the one hand, looking at classifications and information systems explains how communities of practice identify themselves with adopted technological artefacts. On the other hand, people shape technological artefacts and drive technology evolution, hence technology innovation. However, it is therefore necessary to unveil the mechanisms that make us behave not just as individuals, but as societies. Technology has a pivotal role in connecting individuals. It is necessary to move the analysis from the *micro*, i.e. understanding how individuals or social actors behave with respect to technology, to the *macro*, i.e. understanding how societies or social groups behave with respect to technology.

4.1 Social Accounts of Technologies

How do features emerge in socio-technical systems? What are the means of propagation in socio-technical systems? The theory of classification explains how communities of practice identify themselves with adopted technological artefacts or boundary objects, hence boundary infrastructures [5]. The social shaping of technology theory explains how people shape technological artefacts and drive technology evolution, hence technology innovation [22]. *What then is the missing link? How does the Information Society build up?* It is necessary to unveil the mechanisms that make us behave not only just like individuals, but also like social "animals" [22, 29]. The focus of analysis then moves from the *micro*, i.e. understanding how individuals or social actors behave with respect to technology, to the *macro*, i.e. understanding how societies or social groups behave with respect to technology.

Looking at the micro scale of socio-technical systems, *Distributed Cognition* takes into account how social actors acquire and use resources [10, 26]. Distributed cognition focuses on the interaction between representational resources, which can be located within the human mind as well as external artefacts. It enhances our understanding of how people carry on information mediated activities by using distributed

S. Anderson and M. Felici, *Emerging Technological Risk*,
DOI: 10.1007/978-1-4471-2143-5_4, © Springer-Verlag London Limited 2012

resources. Distributed cognition stresses that human cognition is not isolated within human minds, but relies on external distributed artefacts. Internal and external artefacts do not exist in isolation. They are integral parts of socio-technical systems. A holistic account captures the nature of socio-technical systems.[1]

The characterisation of distributed cognition provides us a simple systemic model of socio-technical systems. *Activity Theory* analyses how *social interactions* influence human cognition [10, 11]. Its recent developments provide an account that further explains how people interact with technology [10, 11]. Activity Theory explains how human beings regulate their behaviour by means of inclusion of auxiliary stimuli into their activities. The stimuli originate in external artefacts or in social interactions. Activity theory, in other words, emphasises that human behaviour should be understood in the context of social interactions and external activities. Any subject (or individual) accomplishes specific activities (or objectives) through negotiations within a social community by processes of *internalisation* and *externalisation*. Internalisation explains how individuals construct internal models of their activities (to be performed). Externalisation explains how individuals design and implement new activities. Communities of practice adopt similar processes (i.e. membership and naturalisation) in shaping boundary objects, that is, artefacts shared by communities. Similarly, processes of *Social Learning* explain how human beings perceive technologies in order to acquire computational artefacts and to accomplish specific activities (or tasks) [30]. Recent research, for instance, analyses Social Learning in multimedia systems [30]. Social Learning, in particular, consists of two main processes, namely, *innofusion* (i.e. learning by trying) and *domestication* (i.e. learning by interacting). The combination of distributed cognition and activity theory enables us to characterise socio-technical systems, although it is still necessary to enhance our ability to "go beyond description to prediction" [10] of emergent socio-technical systems. It is, therefore, important to understand how social networks [7, 12, 15, 24] shape technology and let system properties (e.g. dependability) emerge. Social actors, therefore, use available resources in order to achieve specific objectives and perform their activities within emerging social structures or networks [7, 24].

---

[1] The SHEL model has been adopted in various domains though originally drawn from Avionics and Air Traffic Control (ATC). The guidelines in [6], for instance, take it as a fundamental conceptual model of human factors. The SHEL model defines any (electronic mediated) productive process performed by a combination of hardware (e.g. any material tool used in the process execution), software (e.g. procedures, rules, practices) and liveware (e.g. end-users, managers) resources embedded in a given environment (e.g. socio-cultural, political). Hence, any productive process may be regarded as an instantiation of the SHEL model for a specific process execution. The SHEL model emphasises that any productive process relies on the different resources, distributed cognition and resource-based modelling. These different aspects of socio-technical systems can be linked together in a sound way [31]. Cognition models, moreover, allow the analysis of dangerous conditions or technology interactions [3]. For instance, simple models representing human understandings with respect to socio-technical systems have stimulated the use of mechanised verification methods in order to identify "automation surprises" [27]. The results encourage further investigations of the use of mechanised tools in order to identify inconsistencies into the design of technology interactions.

Technology mediated social networks characterise modern societies (e.g. *Information Society*). Research in social networks investigates networking properties in order to support the design of technology [7]. Sociological accounts, for instance, giving rise to the *Actor-Network Theory* (ANT) [14, 22, 29], explain the social link between *social actors* and heterogeneous entities (e.g. classification systems [4]). Social actors perform within their social networks. These *spontaneously emerging* social networks (e.g. *intentional networks* [24]) are essential in the modern technology mediated society. They exploit available *resources* in order to organise other social actors on a large scale [29]. Moreover, social processes which are used for engagement with emerging structures affect risk perception [8]. Therefore, a lack of account of such social networks and group formations exposes socio-technical systems to a set of emergent hazards, due to the nature of such systems, complementary to purely technical hazards. For instance, at the micro level, interactions (that is, micro-level interactions) may give rise to socio-technical hazards related to timing and knowledge distribution [13]. On the other hand, at the macro level, people (by their social networks) may constrain socio-technical systems by collective behaviour and give rise to emergent properties. The analysis of socio-technical systems in the large, that is, at the macro level, enhances our understanding of mechanisms underpinning technology mediated social networks and affecting socio-technical systems.

4.2 System Performativity

Socio-technical systems carry an extent of risk. The traditional view is that risk relates to faults in systems [25, 28]. Risk management usually relies on the frequency of manifestation and severity of the consequences of system flaws. Understanding the risk associated with such systems is difficult and exposes the limitation of traditional approaches to risk, because socio-technical systems are deeply embedded in organisations. Organisations comprise many different groups forming emergent social networks [7, 24], whose risk perception may differ radically and whose needs for and attitude to system change also vary depending on role and environment [8]. Different constitutions of social groupings within organisations shape risk perception [8].

Our studies have, therefore, analysed potential risks in different organisations focusing on how the dominance of particular groups de-emphasises certain classes of hazards.

Two important lines of work arose by taking into account various aspects of socio-technical systems. At the micro level of socio-technical systems, the case studies investigate mechanisms for managing and mitigating the risk of change in complex socio-technical systems. The results allow us to generalise and combine theories (e.g. theory of classification and cultural theory) together with empirical findings pointing out some classes of socio-technical hazards. For example, in a large-scale study of dependable process transfer from one location to another, the results point out that the structure and modularity of organisations (in terms of boundary objects) can pose critical Boundary Hazards for organisations.

In particular, the loss of information across organisational boundaries can expose complex organisations to significant risk. In studying change, our interest lay in exploring hybrid socio-technical approaches to mitigating the risk of change in complex organisations. The emergence of evolutionary structures captures technology trajectories' characterising system evolution resulting from the social shaping of technology [22]. The studies highlight how responsibility and trust are critical aspects affecting work practice as well as technology innovation. Misunderstanding responsibility or developing mistrust expose organisations to emerging technological risk. The results emphasise the role of trust in managing risk and mistrust as a potential source of risk arising from system failures. At the macro level, therefore, it is necessary to highlight how socio-technical systems expose complex organisations to various socio-technical hazards.

The *Long Term Capital Management* (LTCM), at a macroscopic scale of analysis, is a fascinating example of risk in large systems [21]. The studies in [21] take into account lessons drawn from market mechanisms for the construction of large-scale socio-technical systems. The innovative use of a mathematical model for hedge funds in the LTCM, in particular, explores the connection between diversity in computer systems and diversity of portfolio together with social mechanisms that defeat attempts to maintain diversity in a changing market. The in-depth study of the social formation of financial markets provides new insights into the role of social shaping in creating and responding to change in complex organisations. The LTCM study analysed the *performative* nature of finance theory in creating and shaping market interactions. The studies in [21] question the *performativity of economics*. Starting from basic notions of performativity, the studies outline a possible classification of different performativities and how they relate each other. The classification of performativity in [21] consists of four types:

- "Barnesian" performativity defines that the "practical use of an aspect of economics makes economic processes more like their depiction"
- counterperformativity—as opposed to "Barnesian" performativity—defines that the "practical use of an aspect of economics makes economic processes less like their depiction by economics"
- "effective" performativity defines that "the practical use of an aspect of economics has an effect on economic processes"
- "generic" performativity defines that "an aspect of economics (a theory, model, concept, procedure, data set, etc.) is used by participants in economic processes, regulators, etc".

The theoretical development of *option pricing theory*, in particular, has a performative role in financial markets since it appears that as the theory develops and becomes more widely applied, markets begin to conform better to the predictions of the theory.

Part of the work in [21] is a detailed study of the failure of the LTCM and analysis that imitative behaviour across a range of companies engaged in convergence arbitrage created a "superportfolio" held across many firms. This led to instability and a dramatic loss of independence between seemingly quite different holdings that led to the near collapse of the financial system. This study has many lessons for the management of risk in complex organisations, with strong social mechanisms that shape institutions. In particular, the loss of independence exposed such organisations to exacerbated consequences of failures, and facilitated very rapid degradations of organisational robustness and resilience. Although this study concentrates on the constitution of financial markets, the observations and generalisations are applicable to a wide range of social institutions. The classes of risks identified by the LTCM study are poorly understood. We have only begun to understand how to manage such risks. For instance, other studies have emphasised the link between economics and security aspects of technology [1, 2]. In particular, our discussion draws lessons from the investigations of system performativity of large-scale social systems characterised by emerging social networks and features.

4.2.1 Emerging Social Networks

Finance, although adopting theoretical mathematical models, finds explanations in social studies [16]. Two main assumptions, for instance, characterise mathematical formulations of financial markets: the *random walk model* and the *efficient market hypothesis*. The former assumes that stock prices follow an unpredictable path. The latter assesses that markets are efficient, in the sense that prices fully reflect all the available information. The combination of the two hypotheses implies that any change in stock prices depends on new information. This precludes any speculation of the market based on (imaginary) trends and (illegal) insider information arising. A socio-historical account of finance allows the investigation of the (unrealistic) demarcation between the technical and the social aspects of finance [16]. It is possible to characterise the distinction between the social and the technical, in a similar way as the distinction between *N-type* (natural kind) and *S-type* (social kind) terms.

The analysis of arbitrage in the case of LTCM stresses the performative nature of finance by showing the presence of S-type terms. An insider historical analysis highlights the presence of S-type traces in finance [16]:

> An N-type, or "natural kind," term is one in which the application of the term to a particular entity can be thought of as a process in which the empirical properties of the entity are judged against a pattern, and the term is applied or not applied according to the perceived closeness of fit. [...] In contrast, with an S-type, or "social kind," the process of concept application is "performative" [...].

The demarcation is further weakened by three main aspects: the emerging social nature of finance, the distinction between public and private knowledge, and the distinction between trading and gambling. The analysis of the crash of the LTCM highlights the presence of S-type terms in financial mechanisms. These terms emerge as, *self-referential* or *self-validating*, *S-loops*. The subtle nature of social interactions often emerges as covert relationships or dependencies [16]:

> Because of the frequent invisibility of S-loops and because of the dominance of what one might call the epistemology of N-terms, influential positions within sociological theory have frequently ignored the loops of self-reference and self-validation [...].

Loops stress the *performativity* of economics. S-loops, however, may give rise to *positive* as well as, unfortunately, *negative feedback*, hence, *counter-performativity* [19]. The existence of positive and negative feedback further highlights the limits of the performativity of economics [19].

The study of *portfolio insurance* in [19] takes into account two different performativities' meanings: *generic performativity* and *Austinian performativity*. The former, i.e. generic performativity, assumes that economic practices perform markets and other economic relations. The latter, i.e. Austinian performativity, implies that economics describes relationships, hence these relationships are (i.e. exist). The development of portfolio insurance and its contribution to the financial crash emerge as a combination of its intrinsic characteristics in creating positive feedback together with sustaining emerging mistrust in financial markets. This combination triggered a devastating cascade effect augmenting the effect of the financial crash. The crash then provides us an instance of *counterperformativity* [19]. The experience of the crash highlights the contingencies and asymmetries between positive and negative feedback. The asymmetries between positive and negative feedback explain to some extent the deep falls in trust (i.e. increased mistrust) and the slow recovery that often characterise the occurrences of accidents [19]:

> The result of the asymmetry [...] may be that the efficiency of the incorporation into prices of negative information [...] is sometimes less than the efficiency of the incorporation of positive information.

These studies again stress the link between sociological accounts of "modern" societies [14], technology and risk. Feedback, for instance, emerges in economic networks as *externalities* (either positive or negative) [2, 14]. The question then is: *how do social networks (or structures) emerge?* The ANT highlights social links (e.g. personal relationships) [29]. The study of *arbitrage*, "a key process in the practice of financial markets [...]" that "allows markets to be positioned as efficient" even in the presence of irrational investors, points out mechanisms enriching and extending classical social links [18]. Trading by arbitrage intends to exploit price discrepancies.

The study investigates the limitations of the performativity of economics with respect to the sociology of arbitrage [18]. In particular, the analysis involves three main aspects. First, arbitrage is a practice conducted by people, who are often personally known to each other and have established interpersonal relationships due to their trading cooperation or competition over the years. Second, emergent behaviour highlights contingent interactions due to *imitation* strategies. Finally, arbitrage presents some limitations in supporting the performativity of economics. It provides limited explanations for the convergence of the discrepancy of prices in financial markets. The study, motivated by the sociology of science in unveiling scientific knowledge, opens the 'black-box' of economics practices [18]. Despite the adoption of mathematical tools in economics practices, the sociology of trading highlights subtle mechanisms undermining the performativity of economics. It is evident how social interactions affect trading. These interactions often emerge as collective actions and perceptions. Personal feelings (e.g. trust or mistrust) and strategies of imitations affect trading in financial markets. The resolution of the collective actions in terms of imitation undermines diversity in economics practices. This reduced diversity (or convergence) triggers high correlation, hence, less robustness and resilience in economics practices. Emerging global microstructures (or social networks), due to imitative arbitrage, characterise financial markets. The wide diversity, both internationally and across asset classes, was affected by the irreversible emergence of correlated risk due to the effects of a global microstructure. The crash of LTCM investments is, to some extent, the result of the financial markets taking into account the emergence of globalisation phenomena [18]:

> Globalization is not a once-and-for-all event, not a unidirectional process, not something that can be stopped, but a composite of a myriad microstructures, often contradictory, waxing and waning.

4.2.2 Emerging Social Behaviour

The characterisation by the ANT exposes the limitations of the performativity of economics [17]. The analysis of the (Black–Scholes or Black–Scholes–Merton, from the names of the contributors) *option pricing equation* questions whether financial economics is performative, rather than the result of economic practices and culture. The investigation highlights the role of bricolage in the formulation of the option pricing equation. Despite the mathematical foundations, the option pricing equation

captures the struggle of other models (e.g. the Capital Asset Pricing Model) to identifying a solution to the option pricing problem. The equation captures the different
attempts for understanding and sampling emerging behaviour in economics practices,
rather than the subsequent mathematical formulations. The *diversity* and the struggle
around the different underlying assumptions and mathematical formulations at the
end represented a source of robustness, rather than weakness. The importance of
the option pricing equation resides in its ability not to describe economics practices,
rather than forging them. This reflexive behaviour characterises the performativity of
the option pricing equation. However, performativity itself provides a limited account
of the nature of financial economics.

> The unfolding of the formulation of the option pricing equation and its adoption
> as economics practices highlight that *irrational* human beings inhabit financial
> markets. A socio-historical account of the option pricing equation highlights
> the limitations of conventional accounts of rational actors or human beings,
> which require, in order to be representative as inhabitants of social networks,
> both impoverishing and enriching [23]:
>
>> A necessary impoverishment is the acknowledgement of humans' limited
>> information-processing and calculational capacity and thus the recognition that a
>> key role is played by simplifying concepts [...] That concepts and material means
>> are constitutive of economic action that economic action is distributed cognition [...]
>> implies that the economic theory crystalized in concepts and devices can indeed be
>> performative, even if not [...] in any simple sense of self fulfilling prophecy, but as
>> the outcome of a conflictual, embedded process. Enrichment of conventional models
>> of the rational actor also seems necessary [...] The critical necessary enrichment
>> is the recognition that the monetary economy is ultimately inseparable from the
>> "economy of regard" [...] in almost all the markets [...] Even in financial markets,
>> the apparent epitomes of self-interested, rational individualism, human beings have
>> remained mutually susceptible [...], and reputation and respect have mattered.
>
> This provides a solution to the problem of *collective action* [17]: "collective
> action, in other words action that advances the interests of an entire group but
> in regard to which the rational egoist will free-ride."

Social actors exhibit *bounded rationality* [9], which explains why they behave
according to a combination of rational information and perceived feelings (e.g. trust
or risk perception). Thus, the problems emerging in economics practices are problems
of *configuration* [17]:

> the financial markets remain [...] an only partially configured world. The struggles to
> configure that world, and the forces opposing and undermining that configuring, are, and
> will remain, at the heart of the history of our times.

The historical accounts of *rational* behaviour point out how social beings expose
the limitations of the performativity of economics [23]. Therefore, risk in economics
is related to practices. Although mathematical modelling supports economics prac-

tices, formal risk controls and cultural memories that have been embedded into economics practices due to processes of social memories (or past experience)— "Option pricing theory has altered how risk is conceptualized, by practitioners as well as by theorists" [17].

It is evident that various interactions constrain economics practices. Nowadays, interactions are often mediated by technology (e.g. telephone and e-mails). The analysis of these interactions or *social connectivities*, in accordance with ANT, highlights three main aspects: *mutual susceptibility, imitation* and *consolidation of hard social links* [20]. Technology enables social interactions. However, the outcomes of these interactions still depend on personal relationships, or mutual susceptibility, established between peers according to previous experience. Therefore, mutual susceptibility or similar forms of interactions (e.g. trust or mistrust) mediate social interactions. According to the theory of bounded rationality [9], human beings have limited capacity for reasoning about knowledge (or information). As such, their behaviour may be *irrational*. Fears over consequences or knowledge uncertainties often trigger convergence, or collective actions, in social behaviour. Imitation characterises collective actions in which individuals act to align themselves with general knowledge (information). These collective actions, in the form of imitation, let global social structures emerge. These social structures (of imitation) are self-reinforcing. Technology often mediates these social interactions or structures. If social actors are able to hold and mobilise those technology enabling social interactions, the emerging social structures become stable. The stability of the emerging social links characterise *hard societies* differentiating them from *soft societies*, in which social links tend to be fragile and volatile [29].

4.3 Performativity Hazards

Emerging social networks expose the limitations of purely technological (or theoretical) accounts of socio-technical systems. In particular, socio-technical systems, at macro level, exhibit particular properties due to emerging social networks. Social networks extend technology. The analysis of such properties allows us to identify a class of hazards due to mechanisms that similarly expose the limitations of performativity, hence, *Performativity Hazards*. Table 4.1 describes the main identified Performativity Hazards: *positive (negative) feedback* and *imitation behaviour*.

The study of socio-technical systems at macro level highlights contingencies between emerging social networks and overall system properties. The results drawn from the study of the limitations of the performativity of economics stress the social aspects of large-scale systems. The social nature of finance (stressed by the distinction between N-type terms and S-type terms) highlights similarities between modern financial markets and large socio-technical systems [16]. The emergence of social connectivities (e.g. mutual susceptibility, imitation and hard networks), or generally speaking social networks, characterises global financial markets [20]. Mechanisms (e.g. performativity and counterperformativity) underlying and emerging in social

Table 4.1 Performativity hazards

Hazard	Description
Feedback: positive or negative	Social networks expose the limitations of system performativity (e.g. that a system is what it is declared to be) by the emergence of positive or negative feedback. On the one hand, positive feedback may strengthen system features (e.g. stability and dependability). On the other hand, negative feedback may undermine system features and expose organisations to failures
Social connectivity	It is important to understand how social connectivities extend technical systems. Technology mediates social interaction. Therefore, it is necessary to understand the nature of the social connectivities involved and supported by technology. Social connectivity affects the perception of risk with respect to technology
Imitation behaviour	Social networks make systems susceptible and vulnerable to collective actions resulting in imitating behaviour. The emergence of imitating behaviour affects system diversity and reduces independence across social networks

networks expose the limitations of technological accounts of risk [17, 19]. Similar limitations arise for the performativity of financial markets due to the emerging behaviour spreading across social networks [18, 23].

The combination of negative feedback with imitation behaviour in social networks, that is, emerging social connectivities, lets undependabilities emerge. This combination results in reduced diversity across social networks and strengthening of vulnerabilities, and gives rise to socio-technical failures. Note that similar mechanisms in the presence of positive feedback may introduce resilience in socio-technical systems. Moreover, the hardening of social relationships creates stable social networks. This process is similar to the one creating stable communities of practice around boundary objects. Therefore, communities of practice build strength by adopting technology, although they became vulnerable in the presence of negative feedback that undermines system dependability.

4.3.1 Addressing Performativity Hazards

The analysis of socio-technical systems at the macro level highlights Performativity Hazards due to the underlying mechanisms characterising social networks. Hence, it is possible to identify some strategies in order to mitigate this class of hazards. First, it is necessary to understand the contingencies between social networks and technology. Understanding subtle interactions unveils mechanisms sustaining either positive or negative feedback. Therefore, technology and mitigation actions need to take into account the feedback propagating through emerging social networks. Second, it is necessary to maintain diversity in emerging social networks. On the one hand, reduced diversity facilitates clustering of social networks around technology and supports common work practices. On the other hand, it exposes socio-technical systems to structural vulnerabilities by increasing dependency in social networks. This becomes an unfavourable situation in the presence of negative feedback exaggerated by imitation behaviour across social networks. Understanding these mechanisms enhances our ability to assess the impact of technology with respect to social networks which expose technology innovation to Performativity Hazards.

References

1. Anderson R (2001) Why information security is hard—an economic perspective. In: Proceedings of the 17th annual computer security applications conference, ACSAC 2001. IEEE Computer Society, pp 358–365. doi:10.1109/ACSAC.2001.991552
2. Anderson R, Moore T (2007) The economics of information security: A survey and open questions. In: Proceedings of the fourth bi-annual conference on the economics of the software and internet industries
3. Besnard D, Greathead D, Baxter G (2004) When mental models go wrong: co-occurrences in dynamic, critical systems. Int J Hum Comput Stud 60(1):117–128. doi:10.1016/j.ijhcs.2003.09.001
4. Bowker GC, Star SL (1998) Building information infrastructures for social worlds—the role of classifications and standards. In: Ishida T (ed) Community computing and support systems, no. 1519 in LNCS. Springer, Berlin, pp 231–248. doi:10.1007/3-540-49247-X_16
5. Bowker GC, Star SL (1999) Sorting things out: classification and its consequences. The MIT Press, Cambridge
6. CAA (2002) CAP 719—Fundamental human factor concepts. Civil Aviation Authority
7. Churchill EF, Halverson CA (2005) Social networks and social networking: guest editors' introduction. IEEE Internet Comput 9(5):14–19. doi:10.1109/MIC.2005.103
8. Douglas M, Wildavsky A (1982) Risk and culture: an essay on the selection of technological and environmental dangers. University of California Press, Berkeley
9. Gigerenzer G, Todd PM, TheABC Research Group (1999) Simple heuristics that make us smart. Oxford University Press, New York
10. Halverson CA (2002) Activity theory and distributed cognition: or what does CSCW need to DO with theories? Comput Support Coop Work 11(1–2):243–267. doi:10.1023/A:1015298005381
11. Kaptelinin V, Nardi BA (2006) Acting with technology: activity theory and interaction design. The MIT Press, Cambridge
12. Klein HK, Kleinman DL (2002) The social construction of technology: structural considerations. Sci Technol Hum Values 27(1):28–52. doi:10.1177/016224390202700102
13. Küster Filipe J, Felici M, Anderson S (2003) Timed knowledge-based modelling and analysis: on the dependability of socio-technical systems. In: Proceedings of HAAMAHA 2003, 8th international conference on human aspects of advanced manufacturing: agility & hybrid automation, pp 321–328
14. Latour B (2003) Is re-modernization occurring—and if so, how to prove it? A commentary on Ulrich Beck. Theory Cult Soc 20(2):35–48. doi:10.1177/0263276403020002002

15. Licoppe C, Smoreda Z (2005) Are social networks technologically embedded? How networks are changing today with changes in communication technology. Soc Netw 27(4):317–335. doi:10.1016/j.socnet.2004.11.001
16. MacKenzie D (2001) Physics and finance: S-terms and modern finance as a topic for science studies. Sci Technol Hum Values 26(2):115–144. doi:10.1177/016224390102600201
17. MacKenzie D (2003) An equation and its worlds: bricolage, exemplars, disunity and performativity in financial economics. Soc Stud Sci 33(6):831–868. doi:10.1177/0306312703336002
18. MacKenzie D (2003) Long-term capital management and the sociology of arbitrage. Econ Soc 32(3):349–380. doi:10.1080/03085140303130
19. MacKenzie D (2004) The big, bad wolf and the rational market: portfolio insurance, the 1987 crash and the performativity of economics. Econ Soc 33(3):303–334. doi:10.1080/0308514042000225680
20. MacKenzie D (2004) Social connectivities in global financial markets. Environ Plan D Soc Space 22(1):83–101. doi:10.1068/d317t
21. MacKenzie D (2006) An engine, not a camera: how financial models shape markets inside technology. The MIT Press, Cambridge
22. MacKenzie, D, Wajcman, J (eds) (1999) The social shaping of technology. 2nd edn. Open University Press, Philadelphia
23. MacKenzie D, Millo Y (2003) Constructing a market, performing theory: the historical sociology of a financial derivatives exchange. Am J Sociol 109(1):107–145. doi:10.1086/374404
24. Nardi BA, Whittaker S, Schwarz H (2002) NetWORKers and their activity in intensional networks. Comput Support Coop Work 11(1–2):205–242. doi:10.1023/A:1015241914483
25. Neumann PG (1995) Computer related risks. The ACM Press, New York
26. Norman DA (1993) Things that make us smart: defining human attributes in the age of the machine. Perseus Books, Cambridge
27. Rushby J (2002) Using model checking to help discover mode confusions and other automation surprises. Reliab Eng Syst Saf 75(2):167–177. doi:10.1016/S0951-8320(01)00092-8
28. Storey N (1996) Safety-critical computer systems. Addison-Wesley, Harlow
29. Strum S, Latour B (1987) The meanings of social: from baboons to humans. Inf Sci Soc 26:783–802
30. Williams R, Stewart J, Slack R (2005) Social learning in technological innovation: experimenting with information and communication technologies. Edward Elgar, England
31. Wright PC, Fields RE, Harrison MD (2000) Analyzing human–computer interaction as distributed cognition: the resource model. Hum Comput Interact 15(1):1–41. doi:10.1207/S15327051HCI1501_01

Part III
Emerging Technological Risk

Chapter 5
Hardening Social Links

Technology innovation exposes organisations, like the ones in the healthcare domain, to complex socio-technical hazards. Our studies address a number of aspects of dependability in healthcare settings. The learning outcomes of the review of these studies with respect to the identified emerging technological hazards, i.e. Boundary Hazards, Evolutionary Hazards and Performativity Hazards, are twofold. On the one hand, socio-technical failures affect healthcare settings, which provide rich environments and samples of emerging technological risk. On the other hand, the revision of case studies drawn from the healthcare domain allows us to assess how emerging technological hazards characterise such complex settings. Hence, the analysis of healthcare studies driven by the emerging technological hazards enhances our understanding about the risk of technology innovation.

5.1 Complex Socio-Technical Settings

Healthcare represents a domain in which dependability is of considerable public concern and policy importance [41]. It is clear that technology innovation is expected to play an increasingly important role in the delivery of promised service improvements. Policy makers are looking at technology in order to provide major benefits, e.g.: direct support of patient care; reporting, organising and locating clinical information; coordinating and managing patient healthcare; cost reduction; organisational integration and so on. Unfortunately, technology innovation with its subtle *unforeseen* interaction exposes organisations to complex socio-technical failures. Subtle interactions between technology and organisations highlight the socio-technical nature of failures in such complex domains [33]. Various studies (e.g. see [29, 33, 45]) concern dependability aspects of a number of healthcare systems that have 'failed' in various ways. They examine different classes of healthcare systems and potential types of failures. Although preliminary investigations often identify 'human errors' as principal causes of system failures [29], a systemic view, broadening the Human-Computer Interaction (HCI) to organisational perspectives, highlights several causal

S. Anderson and M. Felici, *Emerging Technological Risk*,
DOI: 10.1007/978-1-4471-2143-5_5, © Springer-Verlag London Limited 2012

factors [28, 30, 33, 42].Taking into account a systemic view of such failures requires us to understand the social aspects of technology innovation. Social accounts of technology innovation would be enabling, enriching, complementing and enhancing for risk analysis [29, 45, 46]. Risk analysis, unfortunately, is often driven by technology arguments providing limited accounts of organisational and social issues relevant to technology innovation. Standards and processes formalising risk analysis would benefit from a complementary account of emerging socio-technical hazards [5].

Social aspects of technology enhance our understanding of *emerging technological risk*. In particular, a social perspective to technology enables the underpinning of various classes of socio-technical hazards, namely, *Boundary Hazards*, *Evolutionary Hazards* and *Performativity Hazards*, complementing current risk assessment methodologies. Boundary Hazards highlight the vulnerabilities of organisational boundaries. Technology often exposes organisations to the propagation of hazards across organisational boundaries. Moreover, the risk also lays in the shift of responsibilities across organisational boundaries and in the raising of mistrust across divisions of labour. Evolutionary Hazards emerge in a lack of understanding of technology trajectories as results of the social shaping of technology. Finally, technology nowadays mediates social connectivities. Social networks extend technology and expose organisations to emerging hazards (e.g. negative feedback and imitation behaviour), which could contribute towards hardening social links and establishing hard homogeneous communities reducing diversity and structural resilience. These classes of socio-technical hazards allow the characterisation of emerging technological risk in complex socio-technical settings. Different case studies drawn from a complex domain, such as Health care, show how such socio-technical hazards enhance our understanding of the risk associated with evolving technology. Hence, the identified classes of socio-technical hazards (i.e. Boundary Hazards, Evolutionary Hazards and Performativity Hazards) provide, that is, underpin, a characterisation about the risk of technology innovation. The findings extend, that is, complement, technology-driven risk analysis.

5.2 Organisational Knowledge

Boundary Hazards arise from misunderstandings or lack of support for processes of organisational knowledge or memory. Studies of organisational knowledge are patchy and often lack empirical analysis of work practice [1, 2]. Discussions often involve debates of what constitutes local (micro) and global (macro) knowledge. Although the distinction between local and global could be artificial, it emphasises the analysis of organisational knowledge at different levels of granularity, e.g. at the micro level, where individuals use technology artefacts enabling organisational memory to be (re)used, or at the macro level, where groups of people (or communities of practice) shape technology artefacts enabling organisational knowledge to be shared. However, organisational knowledge (memory) involves both technology artefacts storing knowledge and processes enabling knowledge management and reuse [1, 2].

Taking into account a social perspective of technology, therefore, allows us to investigate how organisations 'transfer' knowledge by technology innovation [19]. Failing to understand the underlying mechanisms (in terms of boundary objects and processes of enabling organisational knowledge) and their social perspectives exposes organisations to the risk of Boundary Hazards, perhaps emerging as undependabilities such as technology failures, mispractices (e.g. 'human errors') or reduced services. The analysis draws on healthcare case studies and points out contingencies between dependability and the mechanisms underlying organisational knowledge. The results enhance our understanding of the nature of Boundary Hazards.

5.2.1 Knowledge Management

Work practices stress the role of managing resources that enable knowledge management at organisational level. The characterisation of work practices with respect to boundary objects, in particular technology artefacts, allows us to analyse how the coordination of activities, social interactions and interactions with artefacts enable knowledge management. A study of *bed management* in hospital settings emphasises how social interactions and artefacts enable organisational knowledge [17].The study in [17] investigates how hospital managers interacting with a *Management Information System* (MIS) need to overcome system limitations and organisational knowledge gaps in order to address critical conditions such as short availability of beds and implementation of contingency plans. Unforeseen (e.g. accidents) as well as seasonal events (e.g. winter fevers) may stretch hospital capacities and service performances. Therefore, the managerial activity is crucial in order to address contingencies and meet governmental service targets.

The information system, in the case study, provided a daily report of the bed availability. However, the report took into account only expected predictions according to generally available information. Therefore, hospital managers developed common practices in order to address a *bed crisis*. These practices involved going around and counting the *available* beds and checking the *beds board*. The beds board is available to people attending the ward and managers. However, the status of each bed depends on the status of the patient. Therefore, the classification of beds, provided by the MIS, as "free" or "occupied", failed to take into account those situations in which a patient may be due to be discharged. In order to acquire a more accurate figure and further information than the one provided by the system, hospital managers also needed to consult staff attending the ward about those beds likely to become available. The analysis highlights how local boundary objects, such as the beds board, general ones, such as the MIS and work practices enable a system of *calculability*, which is afforded in the hospital setting [17]. Such representations must be understood as embedded within the practicalities of the setting, and that any assumed benefits of replacing existing systems must be carefully considered.

Figure 5.1 shows a representation of the knowledge management case study in terms of boundary objects and communities of practice. It highlights how social

Fig. 5.1 Boundary objects, communities of practices and social interactions involved in knowledge management and coordination

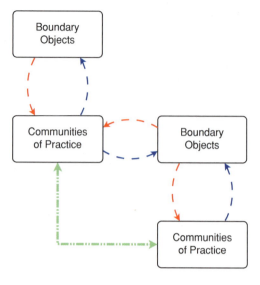

interactions enable the coordination between global and local knowledge, or recipient boundary objects.

Changing the configuration by the introduction of new technology, for instance, an integrated management information system, which integrates both global and local artefacts, i.e. boundary objects, requires a careful consideration of the social collaborations extending and enabling communication means for knowledge sharing. For instance, a new information system that simply integrates information means (e.g. information management system and beds board) may support social interactions by simply making information available remotely. On the other hand, a different solution may take into account a different bed classification, which takes into account both the clinical trajectory of a patient and the one of a bed. The resulting trajectory will highlight a classification system which takes into account additional (e.g. clinical) information that is usually provided by direct social communication. However, the emphasis is that knowledge management is embedded in work practices and used artefacts. Technology innovation needs to take into account trade offs, balances as well as interactions achieved in work practices.

5.2.2 Knowledge Embedding

Knowledge management strategies often advocate and rely on the adoption of electronic records supporting information sharing and integration. There are controversial assumptions underlying the adoption of technology as information infrastructure. First, information sharing intends to support organisational visibility. However, this puts little emphasis on the meaning of available information (across and within) organisations (or organisational boundaries and divisions of labour), assuming a general common understanding by people accessing information. Second, it undermines work practices around artefacts, or boundary objects, storing information. This is tightly coupled with work practices proving a means of interpreting available information and updating it. The analysis of information records in medical settings stresses that work practices and relevant information artefacts expose the limitations of strategies simply advocating the adoption and migration to an *Electronic Medical Record* (EMR) in order to support information sharing and organisational knowledge [14, 18, 26].

The underlying assumptions of adopting an EMR strategy imply that organisations will benefit from shared knowledge and increased visibility across different communities of practice. Unfortunately, the analysis of work practices in a medical setting (a toxicology ward within a UK hospital) highlights how information records depend on the social interactions enabling decision-making processes and organisational knowledge [26]. In particular, it stresses the role of information records as boundary objects. However, their knowledge repository functionality depends on the ability of people to access them and to interpret them. They represent a written story of the clinical processes forging patient trajectories [18]. Therefore, their stored knowledge derives from negotiations, interpretations and decisions taken by staff accessing and updating records throughout clinical processes [18]. These processes rely on social relationships and perceived reliance (e.g. trust) established over different interactions [14, 18]. Work practices depend on established social interactions that demonstrate the practical accomplishment of various kinds of work, in particular their role as intermediaries with responsibilities and expertise shaping clinical trajectories [26]. Social interactions negotiate and adjust patient trajectories through existing social connectivities, often technology mediated.

Issues arise in knowledge sharing due to awareness, availability, accessibility and locality [26]. These issues fall into two main categories of knowledge and social relationships. The first concern is knowing whether or not information is actually available. The second one is whether or not social relationships exist in order to gather required knowledge. Moreover, social relationships (e.g. trust) often mitigate emerging issues [14]. For example, it is possible that different staff members require access to the same records. Therefore, members can still negotiate and access the same records in different ways (e.g. concurrent accessing without disturbing ongoing work, splitting records into different parts, and coping records). However, social interactions often serve to acquire new information filling knowledge gaps in the records. Analysing emerging trajectories may provide useful information for understanding organisational failures.

Looking at information records, for instance, should enable clinical staff to see the status of a patient and calculate where in the organisational and temporal cycle of events surrounding an illness trajectory that particular patient might be. Work practices distinguish the various statuses by the careful balancing and articulating complex mutually related tasks. In the process trajectory, the patient record represents a particular and suitable organisational representation of the current state of affairs. Therefore, the representation, storage and transmission of information, by whatever means, need to take account of social interactions within work settings and information usages.

   Knowledge integration is a complex goal. Although technology, such as the EMR, supports to some extent its achievement, issues may undermine its potential benefits. Processes of technology innovation need to accommodate both (co-evolving) work practices and technologies. Technology innovation changes work practices, which feed back into technology itself [26]. Information records represent organisational boundary objects, or boundary infrastructures. They are accessible for those who know how to use them. This highlights the professional membership and relationship between boundary objects and communities of practice. Moreover, they constitute a means of achieving performance activities for which organisations are accountable in various ways. The analysis shows that much organisational knowledge is often emerging from procedures and interactions. Embedding knowledge in technological artefacts needs to understand contingent aspects in work practices. Knowledge is a matter of organisational relevance. Technology that intends to capture organisational knowledge needs to take into account complex conceptual and empirical issues in work practices. It is important to understand how technology innovation alters exiting social links within organisations. Although it can strengthen social relationships, from soft to hard links [44], it may introduce contingent feedback, either positive or negative, into organisations by establishing, supporting or favouring other emerging interactions.

5.3 Technology Interaction

Organisational knowledge [1, 2], grounded in the theories of distributed cognition and activity theory [24, 31], highlights the role of technology artefacts, or boundary objects, in capturing process trajectories of work practices. On the one hand, boundary objects enable and support social interaction among communities of practice. On the other hand, the social shaping of boundary objects (i.e. contextualisation, decontextualisation and recontextualisation of knowledge [1, 2]) captures technology trajectories. Hence, the mitigation (emergence) of *Evolutionary Hazards* depends, to a certain extent, on the ability (deficiency) of coordinating such processes and making knowledge available when necessary in order to perform critical activities. This highlights two main aspects of technology interaction: *knowledge rationality* and *knowledge timing*. The former emphasises how the interaction with technology affects reasoning about knowledge (i.e. processes of distributed cognition recollecting knowledge). The latter highlights a process viewpoint of technological interaction. Behaviours of *bounded rationality* [23] emerge in reasoning with technology. Knowledge availability depends on how technology artefacts embed knowledge as well as on how social interactions (re)distribute knowledge.

5.3.1 Knowledge Rationality

Organisational knowledge emerges from the coupling between boundary objects, embedding knowledge, and work practices shaping them and filling knowledge gaps by social interactions. *Distributed cognition* characterises processes of reasoning about knowledge embedded into technology artefacts. However, bounded rationality characterises our ability to process knowledge [23]. Understanding the underlying (knowledge reasoning) mechanisms is important in order to asses the implications of introducing new (e.g. detection) technology in work settings. Taking into account social aspects of work practices provides new insights into technology interaction [25]. In particular, it enhances our understanding of the effects of technology on human performance (e.g. in terms of error rates) and addresses critical contingencies [27]. It highlights work practices and eases acceptance by communities of practice [27, 38]. Moreover, it provides further information supporting work practices and policies for how technology would be actually used, for example, distinguishing between detection and diagnosis activities. Finally, it points out contingencies between trust (in technology) and (human) performance [3, 4, 43]

Technology intends to support human activities, although technology interaction presents contingencies undermining the overall objectives (e.g. in terms of increased safety and human performance). Unfortunately, technology interaction affects organisational knowledge as well as performance. The study of *Human-Machine Interaction* (HMI), in a mammography case study, provides interesting insights into how hybrid or heterogeneous systems, that is, socio-technical systems, 'fail' [43]. It considers a systemic view of the *composed* human machine system. The operator uses the output of a *Computer Aided Detection* (CAD) tool in order to provide a clinical judgement about whether or not to recall a patient for further screening. There are four different possible outcomes of screening tests [22]. Decision-making errors fall in two different types of failures: *false negative* decisions, in which a patient with cancer is not recalled and *false positive* ones, in which a healthy patient is recalled. When a person has a disease, the test can be either positive (a *true positive*) or negative (a *false negative*). The probability of true positive is the *sensitivity* of the test. Conversely when a person does not have a disease, the test can be either positive (a *false positive*) or negative (a *true negative*). The probability of the true negative is the *specificity* of the test. The rates of the two outcomes, i.e. the *sensitivity* and the *specificity*, add up to one. Note that "two of the four possible outcomes [...] are dependent on one another: Decreasing the false positive rate of a test increases the false negative rate, and vice versa. The four probabilities are called conditional probabilities [...]" [22].

Diversity modelling [35], originating from *software reliability engineering*, highlights contingencies in failure modes. Analysing human machine diversity, in particular, highlights failure mechanisms of particular classes of socio-technical systems and contingencies in technology interaction [43]. The modelling stresses that general probabilities fail to capture emergent failure behaviour. Although decision-making is independent from system support, the assumption of *failure independence* is

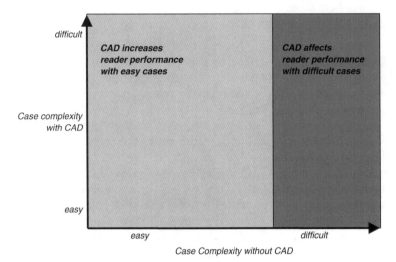

Fig. 5.2 Impact of CAD on different categories of cases

too simplistic. Assuming an extent of dependency implies conditional failures in computer-aided human decisions [43]. However, conditional failure highlights contingencies with respect to the *complexity* of examined cases. That is, some decisions are as difficult with or without computer aid. In particular, failure profiles vary depending on classes of cases. Figure 5.2. shows a schematic representation of the results. CAD support increases reader performance with easy cases. Unfortunately, it affects reader performance with difficult cases. Hence, it is essential in modelling to use detailed conditional probabilities capturing technological interaction on demand, rather than marginal probabilities. It is evident that dependencies and contingencies undermine any applicability of failure independence. However, diversity modelling still presents contingencies with respect to technology evolution or changes in work practices. The probabilistic account also points out *uncertainty* in decision-making.

Although technology interaction exposes the limitations of diversity modelling, it was useful to drive further empirical analysis uncovering fallacies in the assumptions underlying computer-aided decision support [3, 4]. Further empirical analysis highlights uncertainty in the hypothesis that computer-aided decision tools increase the *sensitivity* of less qualified readers without adversely affecting their *specificity*. The probabilist analysis of human and machine performance was based of different accounts of failure rates [3]:

> Note that sensitivity and specificity are defined differently for the human and the machine. For the human the sensitivity is the proportion of cancers that are recalled (for further assessment) and for the machine it is the proportion of cancers that it correctly prompts. Specificity is, for humans, the proportion of normal cases that are not recalled and, for the machine, the proportion of normal cases that are not prompted.

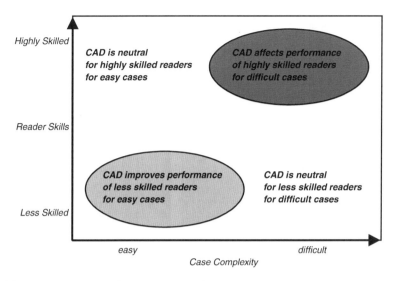

Fig. 5.3 Impact of CAD on different categories of readers

The underlying idea is to assess whether or not practitioners (especially radiographers) with computer-aided decision support could replace expert ones as second readers [25]. This intends to improve overall performance at reduced cost. In particular, the analysis highlights contingencies in system usage, although the system is intended to support decision-making without worsening the overall performance (in terms of specificity). Figure 5.3. shows a schematic representation of the results.

Two important results follow from the analysis. First is that decision-making processes are sensitive to difficult cases in which both the system and the reader fail. That is, the complexity of the examined cases affects the specificity of both human and machine. Moreover, the analysis points out differences between highly skilled and less skilled readers. Less skilled readers benefit from CAD support for simple cases whereas CAD support is ineffective for the complex ones in which both less skilled readers and machine fail. In this case, therefore, CAD support is neutral for less skilled readers for difficult cases. Unfortunately, CAD support affects the sensitivity of highly skilled readers for difficult cases. This contradicts the general assumption that CAD support is 'beneficial for all readers'. Second is that performance depends on *trust in automation*. Further analysis highlights that decision uncertainty is due to trust in automation. This highlights that *overtrust* (or *misplaced trust*) in automation, or computer support, may give rise to failures or affect overall performances [43]. Overtrust or misplaced trust can undermine the benefits of decision support. Finally, system usages undermined the hypothesis of independence on technology interaction. Technology responses affect user behaviour. For instance, users acquire system responses in order to reduce uncertainty or gain confidence over their decisions. Expectations arose once users acquired further understanding of the system sensitivity, limitations or mechanisms of failures. The

Fig. 5.4 CAD communities of practice and their technology interaction

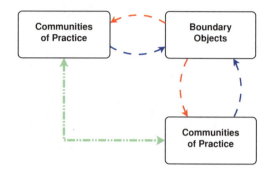

results highlight a pattern of technology interaction. In particular, the analysis of tests (grouped according to their complexity) and users, i.e. readers, (grouped according to their skills) stresses diversity over technology interaction. The emerging *architecture* results in different groups of readers (highly skilled and less skilled) interacting (i.e. shaping) technology artefacts, or boundary objects. They benefit from common arte-facts, if work practices and policies distinguish them by sampling cases according to their complexity. Figure 5.4. shows the emerging socio-technical architecture in terms of communities of practice, boundary objects and social interactions.

Note that social interactions together with social-shaping processes (e.g. contex-tualisation, decontextualisation and recontextualisation of knowledge [1, 2] into boundary objects) between communities of practice and boundary objects, respec-tively, enable organisational knowledge. Therefore, the better technology innovation captures the rich picture of technology interaction, the better the dependability of socio-technical systems. Moreover, work practices and policies, in order to be as effective as possible, need to reflect technology trajectories emerging from tech-nology interaction.

5.3.2 Knowledge Timing

Knowledge availability arises as an emergent property required in order to success-fully accomplish specific tasks. Studies in medical settings place emphasis on how timing aspects of knowledge exhibit contingencies with respect to dependability [6, 7]. In particular, timely social interactions allow knowledge to be available when it is needed. Failing to provide knowledge in a timely fashion can trigger undepend-abilities, hence giving rise to failures [32]. The study in [6, 7] of the introduction of a new medical system within a *Neonatal Intensive Care Unit* (NICU) highlights about how technology mediates social interactions and enables them to share knowledge. The new system is an expert system designed for helping junior doctors to manage (configuration) changes to the ventilators that are used in treating premature babies with respiratory problems. Unfortunately, new technology may be disruptive with respect to established social interactions. It may alter knowledge availability, hence efficiency and performance of work practices. Knowledge timing highlights work practices in terms of process trajectories [15, 16].

The investigations reported in [15, 16] point out how process modelling (i.e. process maps) supports organisational processes (i.e. trajectories) by allocating time, technology and staff efficiently. The analysis of process maps (or trajectories) reflecting work practices allows the identification of emerging evolutionary hazards such as, for instance, "bottlenecks" in *illness trajectories* of patients [15, 16]. Process trajectories are tightly coupled with work practices. The better the coupling the better the *mutual-relevance* and *coordination* among communities of practice and technology artefacts. Ethnomethodology results highlight how process trajectories (i.e. process maps) capture local knowledge [15, 16]. That is, work practices follow process trajectories and provide knowledge in a timely fashion. Failing to understand process trajectories and to support relevant work practices exposes organisations to emerging evolutionary hazards such as, for instance, knowledge mismatches or timing slips. Therefore, transferring them across organisational settings or divisions of labour exposes organisations to boundary hazards as well as evolutionary hazards.

The study in [7] examined the factors that contribute to the dependability of the existing systems and work practices, which deliver neonatal intensive care dependably. It relies on a cognitive task analysis in order to gather major acceptability and dependability requirements for the new system. The analysis consists of three major parts: *domain analysis, light-weight rich picture representation* and *critical decision method*. The domain analysis, involving interviews and observations, highlights work practices within a neonatal unit. It identifies critical work practices that guarantee efficient and dependable responses to emergencies or raised alarms. Note that there are alarms sounding fairly frequently within a NICU. Most of these alarms are caused by spurious (i.e. *false positive*) alarms rather than clinical events. One of the heuristics adopted by clinical staff was the mnemonic *DOPE*, which stands for: Displacement of the endo-tracheal tube (ETT); Obstruction of the ETT; Pneumothorax and Equipment malfunction, before adjusting the ventilator settings. This heuristic captures subsequent activities prioritised according to their criticality.

Bounded rationality justifies the use of "fast and frugal heuristics" in order to deal with uncertainty (in knowledge) and subsequent decision-making under limited resources and time constraints—"Satisficing is a method for making a choice from a set of alternatives encountered sequentially when one does not know much about the possibilities ahead of time", i.e. under *uncertainty*, "Satisficing is a way of making a decision about a set of alternatives that respects the limitations of human time and knowledge. [...] Fast and frugal heuristics", based on satisficing, "employ a minimum of time, knowledge, and computation to make adaptive choices in real environments" [23]. Heuristics are effective methods of limiting the alternative available solutions (i.e. decision choices). Moreover, they guide clinical staff through subsequent activities providing relevant knowledge in order to assess arising alarms and, eventually, to act accordingly.

The study, then, investigates *critical decision-making* processes in order to inform system development [6, 7]. The analysis, based on interviews and observations, highlights decision-making processes among staff with different levels of experience and expertise. It highlights how emerging knowledge and severity drive (hierarchical) decision-making processes often cause shifts in actions. The investigation focuses on two major incidents, described by experts, in which there was a shift in situation assessment. In both cases the change in strategy (i.e. the shift in decision) was due to new information apparently contradicting the prevailing diagnosis of ventilation conditions. In the first case, the new information was the sounding of the ventilator alarm. In the second, it was the results of the manual test that confirmed over-ventilation. Both cases resulted in changes in the configuration of the ventilator. In general, changing the configuration of the ventilator settings involves a process of elimination. Most staff described it using the DOPE mnemonic heuristic to remind them to check for alternative causes of the problem, before adjusting the ventilator. Once the decision to intervene using the ventilator has been made, that is, the process trajectory changes status (or the case is classified accordingly), a number of local procedures follow. The analysis of procedural practices, therefore, highlights contingencies between knowledge timing and dependability emerging as issues affecting process trajectories [6, 16]. The results have two major implications for the new system. First is that the system relies on sensors that may trigger *false positives*. Observations of specific cases highlight the high number of alarms. Hence, the new system should have a low *sensitivity* to noisy data, that is, decrease (or, at least, not increase) the number of false positives. Second is that it should summarise valid and useful information supporting existing work practices, such as the DOPE mnemonic heuristic.

Further analysis of the domain investigated work practices from an organisational viewpoint [7]. It highlights how work practices rely on a hierarchical organisation of roles and responsibilities. Decision-making processes involve these hierarchical organisations depending on the complexity of the decision and individual competences. The analysis allowed the capture of communications and their frequencies. A rich picture representation shows communication links and their frequency of usage between the various staff working in or with the neonatal unit. Most of these communications, happening during formally scheduled (e.g. ward round meeting involving staff from the night shift and staff from the new day shift) as well as informal meetings, allow knowledge sharing. Additionally, written records provide the other major source of information. Similarly, a rich picture representation shows who access which data records and how often. Records, therefore, are mediating artefacts (i.e. boundary objects) enabling knowledge communication and sharing. However, social and technology interactions fill knowledge gaps. It is, therefore, important that the new system supports existing interactions and levels of communication. The new system is an enabling technology for medical staff in decision-making within the neonatal unit. It should reduce the length of time it takes people to learn to make critical decisions. It has, however, to maintain the hierarchical channels of communication identified in the rich pictures.

Work practices around the new system need to guarantee that people use the system support sensibly, that is, without over-trusting automation or decision support. Thus, the new system can support the existing organisational hierarchy (in terms of responsibilities) of decision-making and communication, ensuring that appropriate cases still get referred to the relevant authority. Note that new technology may shift responsibilities across organisational boundaries and divisions of labour. Moreover, it is necessary to record decisions mediated by the new system. Hence, the system should support another system functionality: data recording. This functionality is to support the analysis of process trajectories in order to provide feedback to the organisation and to enable processes of organisational learning. Note that the classification underlying data collection and critical incident reporting needs to capture work practices, that is, communities of practice need to understand the underlying classification system [11]. Otherwise, mismatches between classification and work practices undermine organisational knowledge and expose organisations to boundary hazards as well as evolutionary hazards, hence, increase the risk of socio-technical failures.

5.4 Technology Communities

Technology innovation, or the introduction of new technology, has two main effects. First, on the one hand, technology is empowering technology communities. Second, on the other hand, technology mediates social interactions. These allow communities to strengthen their social links around technology [37, 44]. The more a community adopts technology, the stronger are the social links. The use of technology (computer-based) artefacts characterises the modern *Information Society*. Unfortunately, technology exposes communities to emerging technological hazards. However, emerging social networks [13] and groups affect risk perception [21] and attitude towards technology innovation. Analysing mechanisms underlying technology communities enhances our understanding about how technology enables people, hence, *technology communities*. A lack of understanding exposes people to hazards emerging through social connectivity or other emerging technological risks.

5.4.1 Enabling Technologies

Technology innovation provides the opportunity to enable communities of practice, although it is necessary to understand the complex social settings in order to be as effective as possible. The studies in [12, 20, 39] of domestic systems emphasise how social aspects pose particular challenges to technology design and innovation. In particular, the account of rich and complex social interactions exposes the limitation of purely technical dependability arguments [20]. Although technology innovation is intended to empower communities, it may expose them to emerging technological risk. The study in [39] of services relying on technology for older people highlights a broad spectrum of risks challenging technology innovation. It is, therefore, necessary to capture complex social aspects and to take them into account in designing technology innovation. Moreover, understanding complex social settings extends technology risk analysis and enables the deployment of technology innovation within communities of practice [39].

The design of assistive technology for medication regimes [12], for example, provides an instance of how technology innovation exposes vulnerable communities to emerging technological hazards. Hence, it is necessary to understand complex application domains characterised by rich social interactions. Technology innovation needs to capture, in order to be effective, process trajectories emerging as work practices, otherwise expose people to emerging technological hazards. The studies in [12, 20, 39] emphasise how the design of enabling technology needs to take into account dependability in the wider system. That is, social technologies expose the limitation of technical dependability arguments [20]. Assistive technology, for instance, could be a particular case of such technologies [12]. More in general, technology assists people in different tasks. Understanding the context of use is central for designing technology. Moreover, technology is often delivered to people in order to provide them with tailored support. However, it is necessary to understand the risk involved with technology innovation [39].

5.4.2 Mediating Technologies

Technology innovation empowers communities of practice. One of the results is often the provision to people of new technology mediated interactions [34]. However, social interactions extend technical systems. Moreover, in the modern *Information Society*, social interactions are often technology mediated—email or Internet represent examples of, *modern* [34, 44], technology mediated social connectivity [36]. Understanding how technology enables social connectivity is crucial in order to enable technology communities or specific targeted groups of people [8, 9]. Enabling technological communities intends to harden social links [44]. For instance, e-commerce provides an example of how technology innovation provides new services, therefore, enables social interactions [8, 9].

Providing technology innovation for targeted communities requires an understanding of the social networks [13, 40] around, or being 'formed' by, technology—"an informal community network of support relying on neighbours" [8]. This relies on processes of social shaping of technology, that is, of membership and naturalisation by communities of practice [10]. Note that the way in which social networks and groups adopt technology artefacts has several implications. On the one hand, technology exposes social networks to emerging technological risk. On the other hand, social networks expose the limitations of technology dependability. Understanding emerging socio-technical hazards requires us to unveil the underlying mechanisms characterising technology communities. It is important to understand how technology allows us to cross social barriers in forming technology mediated communities [8]:

> The Net Neighbours scheme addresses barriers to internet access not by assisting with the technology but by appropriating and circumventing the technology. The transaction is

mediated by the volunteer and the only technology that the older person need come into contact with is the telephone. In the Net Neighbours scheme the volunteer is an intermediary rather than a helper, enabler or teacher and in this sense some might argue that the scheme is dis-empowering: it does not encourage older people to get to know and use the technology directly.

Understanding risk in social contexts allows us to deploy *socially dependable technology* [8, 9].

5.5 Hardening Social Links

Emerging technological risk, expressed in terms of *Boundary Hazards*, *Evolutionary Hazards* and *Performativity Hazards*, enhances our understanding of technology innovation. It allows us to analyse the risk involved with technology innovation. This complements and extends technology risk analysis. The revision of different case studies drawn from the Healthcare domain unveils how technology hazards emerge and expose communities of practice. A lack of understanding of the basic mechanisms inhibits and undermines technology innovation. Moreover, it exposes organisations to technology risk. This manifests, for instance, as weak organisational knowledge or problematic technology interaction.

The underpinning of emerging technological risk enhances our understanding of how basic socio-technical mechanisms expose organisations to technology hazards. This provides new insights and understandings of emerging technological risk. The better our understanding of emerging technological risk, the better our ability to deploy technology enabling communities of practices, hence, *hardening social links*. However, it is necessary to understand how technology innovation exposes organisations to new classes of socio-technical hazards. Social aspects of technology expose the limitations of purely technological dependability arguments. The studies of the underlying mechanisms draw some general lessons for understanding and addressing *emerging technological risk*.

References

1. Ackerman MS, Halverson CA (2000) Reexamining organizational memory. Commun ACM 43(1):59–64. doi:10.1145/323830.323845
2. Ackerman MS, Halverson CA (2004) Organizational memory as objects, processes, and trajectories: an examination of organizational memory in use. Comput Support Coop Work 13(2):155–189. doi:10.1023/B:COSU.0000045805.77534.2a
3. Alberdi E, Povyakalo A, Strigini L, Ayton P (2004) Effects of incorrect computer-aided detection (CAD) output on human decision-making in mammography. Acad Radiol 11(8):909–918
4. Alberdi E, Povyakalo AA, Strigini L, Ayton P, Hartswood M, Procter R, Slack R (2005) Use of computer-aided detection (CAD) tools in screening mammography: a multidisciplinary investigation. Br J Radiol 78:S31–40. doi:10.1259/bjr/37646417
5. Anderson S, Koornneef F, Voges U (2003) Risk management for medical devices. Phys Medica 19

6. Baxter GD, Küster Filipe J, Miguel A, Tan K (2005) The effects of timing and collaboration on dependability in the neonatal intensive care unit. In: Redmill F, Anderson T (eds) Constituents of modern system-safety thinking: proceedings of the 13th safety-critical systems symposium, Springer, pp 195–210. doi:10.1007/1-84628-130-X_13

7. Baxter GD, Monk AF, Tan K, Dear PRF, Newell SJ (2005) Using cognitive tack analysis to facilitate the integration of decision support systems into the neonatal intensive care unit. Artif Intell Med 35(3):243–257. doi:10.1016/j.artmed.2005.01.004

8. Blythe M, Monk A (2005) Net neighbours: adapting HCI methods to cross the digital divide. Interact Comput 17(1):35–56. doi:10.1016/j.intcom.2004.10.002

9. Blythe MA, Monk AF, Doughty K (2005) Socially dependable design: the challenge of ageing population for HCI. Interact Comput 17(6):672–689. doi:10.1016/j.intcom.2005.09.005

10. Bowker GC, Star SL (1999) Sorting things out: classification and its consequences. The MIT Press, Cambridge

11. Busse DK, Holland B (2002) Implementation of critical incident reporting in a neonatal intensive care unit. Cogn Technol Work 4(2):101–106. doi:10.1007/s101110200009

12. Cheverst K, Clarke K, Dewsbury G, Hemmings T, Kember S, Rodden T, Rouncefield M (2003) Designing assistive technologies for medication regimes in care settings. Univers Access Inf Soc 2(3):235–242. doi:10.1007/s10209-003-0055-9

13. Churchill EF, Halverson CA (2005) Social networks and social networking: guest editors' introduction. IEEE Internet Comput 9(5):14–19. doi:10.1109/MIC.2005.103

14. Clarke K, Hartswood M, Procter R, Rouncefield M, Slack R (2003) Trusting the record. Methods Inf Med 42(4):345–352

15. Clarke K, Hartswood M, Procter R, Rouncefield M, Slack R, Williams R (2002) Improving 'knife to skin time': process modelling and new technology in medical work. Health Informatics J 8(1):39–42. doi:10.1177/146045820200800107

16. Clarke K, Hughes J, Martin D, Rouncefield M, Sommerville I, Voß A, Procter R, Slack R, Hartswood M (2006) Its about time: temporal features of dependability. In: Clarke K, Hardstone G, Rouncefield M, Sommerville I (eds) Trust in technology: a socio-technical perspective, Comput Supported Coop Work, vol 36, Springer, chap 4, pp 105–121. doi:10.1007/1-4020-4258-2_5

17. Clarke K, Hughes J, Rouncefield M, Hemmings T (2006) When a bed is not a bed: calculation and calculability in complex organizational settings. In: Clarke K, Hardstone G, Rouncefield M, Sommerville I (eds) Trust in technology: a socio-technical perspective, Comput Supported Coop Work, vol 36, Springer, chap 2, pp 21–38. doi:10.1007/1-4020-4258-2_2

18. Clarke KM, Hartswood MJ, Procter RN, Rouncefield M (2001) The electronic medical record and everyday medical work. Health Informatics J 7(3–4):168–170, doi:10.1177/146045820100700310

19. D'Adderio L (2003) Configuring software, reconfiguring memories: the influence of integrated systems on the reproduction of knowledge and routines. Ind Corp Chang 12(2):321–350

20. Dewsbury G, Sommerville I, Clarke K, Rouncefield M (2003) A dependability model for domestic systems. In: Anderson S, Felici M, Littlewood B (eds) Proceedings of the 22nd international conference on computer safety, reliability, and security, SAFECOMP 2003, Springer, no. 2788 in LNCS, pp 103–115. doi:10.1007/978-3-540-39878-3_9

21. Douglas M, Wildavsky A (1982) Risk and culture: an essay on the selection of technological and environmental dangers. University of California Press, US

22. Gigerenzer G (2002) Reckoning with risk: learning to live with uncertainty. Penguin Books, London

23. Gigerenzer G, Todd PM, TheABC Research Group (1999) Simple Heuristics that make us smart. Oxford University Press, New York

24. Halverson CA (2002) Activity Theory and Distributed Cognition: Or What Does CSCW Need to DO with Theories? Comput Supported Coop Work 11(1–2):243–267. doi:10.1023/A:1015298005381

25. Hartswood M, Procter R, Rouncefield M, Slack R (2002) Performance management in breast screening: A case study of professional vision. Cogn Technol Work 4(2):91–100. doi:10.1007/s101110200008

26. Hartswood M, Procter R, Rouncefield M, Slack R (2003) Making a case in medical work: implications for the electronic medical record. Comput Supported Coop Work 12(3):241–266. doi:10.1023/A:1025055829026

27. Hartswood M, Procter R, Rouncefield M, Slack R, Soutter J, Voss A (2003) 'Repairing' the machine: a case study of evaluation of Computer-aided detection tools in breast screening. In: Dourish P, Fitzpatrick G (eds) Proceedings of the eighth European conference on computer supported cooperative work, pp 375–394

28. Hollnagel E (1993) Human reliability analysis: context and control. Academic Press, London

29. Jeffcott MA, Johnson CW (2002) The use of a formalised risk model in NHS information system development. Cogn Technol Work 4(2):120–136. doi:10.1007/s101110200011

30. Johnson C (2002) The causes of human error in medicine. Cogn Technol Work 4(2):65–70. doi:10.1007/s101110200005

31. Kaptelinin V, Nardi BA (2006) Acting with Technology: Activity Theory and Interaction Design. The MIT Press, Cambridge

32. Küster Filipe J, Felici M, Anderson S (2003) Timed knowledge-based modelling and analysis: on the dependability of socio-technical systems. In: Proceedings of HAAMAHA 2003, 8th international conference on human aspects of advanced manufacturing: agility and hybrid automation, pp 321–328

33. Leveson NG (1995) SAFEWARE: System Safety and Computers. Addison-Wesley, Reading

34. Licoppe C, Smoreda Z (2005) Are social networks technologically embedded? How networks are changing today with changes in communication technology. Soc Netw 27(4):317–335. doi:10.1016/j.socnet.2004.11.001

35. Littlewood B, Popov P, Strigini L (2001) Modeling software design diversity: a review. ACM Comput Surv 33(2):177–208. doi:10.1145/384192.384195

36. MacKenzie D (2004) Social connectivities in global financial markets. Environ Plan D: Soc Space 22(1):83–101. doi:10.1068/d317t

37. MacKenzie, D, Wajcman, J (eds) (1999) The Social Shaping of Technology. 2nd edn. Open University Press, Buckingham

38. Martin D, Hartswood M, Slack R, Voss A (2006) Achieving dependability in the configuration, integration and testing of healthcare technologies. comput Supported Coop Work 15(5–6):467–499. doi:10.1007/s10606-006-9032-1

39. Monk A, Hone K, Lines L, Dowdall A, Baxter G, Blythe M, Wright P (2006) Towards a practical framework for managing the risks of selecting technology to support independent living. Appl Ergonomics 37(5):599–606. doi:10.1016/j.apergo.2005.10.003

40. Nardi BA, Whittaker S, Schwarz H (2002) NetWORKers and their Activity in Intensional Networks. Comput Supported Coop Work 11(1–2):205–242. doi:10.1023/A:1015241914483

41. Procter R, Rouncefield M, Balka E, Berg M (2006) Special Issue: CSCW and dependable healthcare systems. Comput Supported Coop Work 15(5–6):413–418. doi:10.1007/s10606-006-9037-9

42. Reason J (1997) Managing the risks of organizational accidents. Ashgate, Aldershot

43. Strigini L, Povyakalo A, Alberdi E (2003) Human-machine diversity in the use of computer advisory systems: a case study. In: Proceedings of the 2003 international conference on dependable systems and networks, DSN'03, IEEE Computer Society, pp 249–258. doi:10.1109/DSN.2003.1209935

44. Strum S, Latour B (1987) The meanings of social: From baboons to humans. Inf Sci Soc 26:783–802

45. Wears RL, Cook RI, Perry SJ (2006) Automation, interaction, complexity, and failure: a case study. Reliab Eng Syst Saf 91(12):1494–1501. doi:10.1016/j.ress.2006.01.009

46. Woods DD, Cook RI (2002) Nine steps to move forward from error. Cogn Technol Work 4(2):137–144. doi:10.1007/s101110200012

Part IV
Conclusions

Chapter 6
Emerging Technological Risk

Technology involves risk. But *what is technology risk?* The literature on risk is broad and involves a vast spectrum of disciplines. It is difficult even to draw a multidisciplinary account of risk. Although different risk accounts might initially seem to be controversial or contradicting each other, it is useful to draw similarities or relationships between them. This supports cross-fertilisation between scientific and practitioner communities, who share an interest in understanding risk in technology and its evolution, or technology innovation. The problem, on the one hand, is a communication one—different disciplines need to inform each other. On the other hand, it requires a shift from multidisciplinary accounts to an interdisciplinary understanding of technology risk. Our socio-technical studies highlight and discuss various research results that contribute towards an interdisciplinary account of *emerging technological risk*.

6.1 Underpinning Technological Risk

The study of *technology risk*, or risk in technology, involves the analysis of how technology exposes society to different threats or hazards. The *risk society* is concerned with how technological hazards affect different groups [2, 3]. Risk complexity manifests in how technology hazards propagate across organisational, or social, boundaries (e.g. division of labour and social classes) [3, 14]. Knowledge about technology informs debate, empowers social groups and allows them to position with respect to technology risk [2]. Various studies (e.g. [2, 3, 13, 14]) investigate and define a broad spectrum of socio-technical accounts of technology risk. These range from a *microscopic* (e.g. how individuals behave with respect to technology and perceive risk) to a *macroscopic* (e.g. organisational, social, socio-political and environmental) analysis of technology risk. Classifications of risk studies (e.g. see [5, 6]) highlight how different accounts of risk lead to different understandings of socio-technical problems.

S. Anderson and M. Felici, *Emerging Technological Risk*,
DOI: 10.1007/978-1-4471-2143-5_6, © Springer-Verlag London Limited 2012

The combination of different levels of investigations (e.g. "micro/meso/macro" [6]) together with diverse approaches and methodologies pinpoints different risk accounts. It identifies different practices of investigating technology risk. Moreover, it allows us to characterise different risks. The problem then is to establish or interpret a link between different levels of analysis together with diverse types of models and approaches, e.g. "normative (or prescriptive)" as opposed to "descriptive" [6]. On the one hand, "complex causalities" that characterise the social dimensions of technology [6] and "complex interactions" [4, 14] may trigger 'unpredictable' failures (or failure modes). On the other hand, the epistemology of the investigations of failures traces back to the causalities leading to accidents [6]. These dimensions, i.e. micro/meso/macro and normative/descriptive, identify a framework for the classification of the modelling approaches underlying the investigations of past accidents [6]. Similarly, it is possible to identify different organisational levels, from "closed system models" to "open system models" [5], for the classification of safety approaches and the underlying models with respect to different social levels of analysis. These classifications position research and investigation methodologies according to 'topologies of socialities' (e.g. micro/meso/macro) and 'system boundaries' (e.g. closed as opposed to open system models) [5, 6].

Disciplinary boundaries between different accounts, unfortunately, inhibit and narrow the scope of analysis of technology risk. This often limits our understanding of technology risk and its underlying mechanisms as a whole. At its simplest, there is a disconnect between different levels of granularities. Drawing similarities and links between different accounts of risk supports cross-fertilisation between scientific and practitioner communities, who seek to understand risk in technology innovation. Unveiling contingencies between the social and the technical enhances our understanding of where socio-technical risks reside.

An interdisciplinary account of *emerging technological risk* seeks to establish links between technical and social accounts of technology risk. Social accounts of risk can be very different, e.g. the economic account begins with the 'individual', whereas the sociological begins with the 'group'—e.g. contrast a 'market' view of risk with a 'cultural' view of risk. We discuss these links in terms of complex *socio-technical hazards*. In order to establish such links, the focus is on the following questions (which are important, but not exhaustive):

• *How does technology cross organisational (e.g. social and cultural) boundaries? How does technology expose organisations to risk across their boundaries?* Understanding the underlying mechanisms of how technology supports different forms of social organisations allows us to address the risk associated with *unbounded* technology (or open system models).

- *How does technology innovation capture evolutionary processes?* Social interaction shapes technology. In order to understand the contingencies between technology innovation and evolutionary processes (characterised by social interaction), it is necessary to unveil how technology innovation affects work practices.
- *How do communities gather together around technology?* It is necessary to understand how communities of practice affect technology development. Accidentally, technology innovation exposes communities of practices to reduced diversity and increased common vulnerability. Hence, it exposes communities of practice to complex system failures (or complex causalities). Understanding the contingencies between the social and the technical requires us to investigate mechanisms of failure propagations across organisational boundaries.

We draw on accounts of risk that contribute towards an interdisciplinary understanding of emerging technological risk. In particular, our account points out research results that fall into the different scales, i.e. microscopic and macroscopic, of analysis. The potential benefit is an interdisciplinary study that links these two scales of analysis. A review of relevant work outlines and emphasises how multidisciplinary work characterises the relationships between scales of analysis. It also assesses the promise of new tools and techniques that arise from interdisciplinary work on emergent risk in socio-technical systems. Our studies identify classes of socio-technical hazards: *Boundary Hazards*, *Evolutionary Hazards* and *Performativity Hazards*. These classes allow us to characterise emerging technological risk. They have origins in, and take into account, multidisciplinary aspects of risk. These classes of socio-technical hazards support risk analysis from microscopic to macroscopic scale, and vice versa. They look at how different risk perspectives affect each other. Hence, they provide an account of technology risk as a whole.

6.2 Classes of Socio-Technical Hazards

Our review of different risk dimensions draws over various multidisciplinary accounts and highlights the complex nature of technology risk. This section summarizes and describes the identified classes of socio-technical hazards: *Boundary Hazards*, *Evolutionary Hazards* and *Performativity Hazards*.

6.2.1 Boundary Hazards

Developing and implementing new organisational information systems necessarily involve reaching agreement, implicitly or tacitly, about knowledge. Various decisions affect how to classify information, how to represent it through the choice of boundary objects and how to access it. The detailed focus upon the design, implementation and use of information systems allows us to consider various opportunities that may exist whether in terms of improved change management procedures or systems to deploy information systems effectively and dependably. Organisations adopt different strategies in order to deal with similar problems with respect to information infrastructures, or boundary objects (infrastructures). Technology solutions address this problem differently, sometimes locally or, at an organisational level. In other cases, organisations adopt existing technology solutions (e.g. Commercial-Off-The-Shelf systems) as established standards or classification systems. However, transfer of knowledge, from its local origin to a standardised classification, or across organisational boundaries and divisions of labour, may affect local knowledge and undermine currently existing work practices.

> Organisations failing to understand and to treat boundary objects (infrastructures) carefully are likely to experience disruptive consequences, which represent significant threats to the dependability of information systems. These hazards may affect knowledge with potential critical consequences for organisational activities and objectives. Technology integration and standardisation, or innovation strategies, although they often involve solutions outside direct scrutiny, expose organisations to a set of hazards across organisational boundaries or divisions of labour, hence *Boundary Hazards*.

6.2.2 Evolutionary Hazards

Technology trajectories emerge as results of evolutionary negotiations involving communities of practice. These negotiations, although involving an extent of technical arguments, involve design decisions as well as social struggles. However, technology innovation consists of cycles of discoveries and exploitations. Further understanding these underlying cycles and mechanisms of technology evolution enhances our ability of managing and configuring technology innovation. The evolutionary nature of technology highlights a class of *evolutionary hazards* (i.e. *evolving work practices, understanding technology trajectories* and *judging moving targets*). The different analysed case studies highlight the coupling between technology and work practices. In particular, work practice and technology co-evolve. On the one hand, technology evolution is driven to some extent by technological innovation. On the other hand, technology innovation is often characterised by social groupings engaging technological as well as political arguments. This emphasises the role of technology as central to organisational information infrastructures. It is critical in order to maintain and support alignment between organisational structures (e.g. in terms of divisions of labours) and objectives (e.g. strategic business targets).

Failing to understand the coupling between technology and work practices poses risk to technology innovation. A lack of understanding of subtle relationships between technology and work practices creates mistrust in technology innovation. Moreover, mechanisms of technology evolution concern divisions of labour, which may exploit, intentionally or accidentally, technology innovation to alter organisational boundaries, e.g. by shifting responsibilities. It is also important to understand how technology innovation (by embedding knowledge into boundary objects or infrastructures) enhances formal as well as informal organisational knowledge supporting communities of practice. Failing to address evolving work practices with respect to technology innovation exposes organisations to *Evolutionary Hazards*, and inhibits opportunities for redundancy and diversity strengthening organisational resilience to complex socio-technical interaction failures.

6.2.3 Performativity Hazards

The study of socio-technical systems at macro level highlights contingencies between emerging social networks and overall system properties. The results drawn from the study of the limitations of the performativity of economics stress social aspects of large-scale systems. The social nature of finance highlights similarities between modern financial markets and large socio-technical systems [7]. The emergence of social connectivities (e.g. mutual susceptibility, imitation and hard networks), or generally speaking social networks, characterises global financial markets [11]. Mechanisms (e.g. performativity and counterperformativity) underlying and emerging in social networks expose the limitations of technological accounts of socio-technical systems [8, 10]. Similar limitations arise for the performativity of economics due to the emerging behaviour spreading across social networks [9, 12].

For instance, the combination of negative feedback with imitation behaviour in social networks, that is, emerging social connectivities, results in reduced diversity across social networks and strengthening of vulnerabilities and gives rise to socio-technical failures. These mechanisms are similar to the ones creating stable communities of practice around boundary objects. Therefore, communities of practice build strength by adopting technology, although they became vulnerable in the presence of negative feedback that undermines system dependability. Socialities expose the limitations of system performativity (e.g. that a system is what it is declared to be) by the emergence of positive (negative) feedback. On the one hand, positive feedback may strengthen system features (e.g. stability, dependability). On the other hand, negative feedback may undermine system features and expose organisations to failures. It is also important to understand how social connectivities extend technical systems and how technology mediates social interaction.

Organisational structures (e.g. social networks) make systems susceptible and vulnerable to collective actions resulting in imitating behaviour. Therefore, it is necessary to understand the nature of the social connectivities involved and supported by technology. Furthermore, social connectivity affects the perception of risk with respect to technology. The emergence of imitating behaviour affects system diversity and reduces independence across communities of practice. Hence, emerging social networks expose the limitations of purely technological (or theoretical) accounts of such systems. In particular, at macro level, socio-technical systems exhibit particular properties due to emerging social networks that extend technology. The analysis of such properties allows us to identify as class of hazards due to mechanisms (e.g. *positive* or *negative feedback* and *imitation behaviour*) that similarly expose the limitations of performativity, hence, *Performativity Hazards*.

6.2.4 Addressing Emerging Technological Risk

The different case studies allow us to identify a set of risk underpinnings, or socio-technical hazards. The investigations of different case studies generalise and assess our findings across different application domains. These findings form the basis for guidelines complementing and extending traditional approaches to technology risk. The guidelines benefit from our comprehensive approach to risk. The empirical, as well as theoretical, nature of our work is such that other industry domains may benefit from our research findings. Social aspects of technology enhance our understanding of *emerging technological risk*. In particular, a social perspective of technology enables the underpinning of various classes of socio-technical hazards.

1. *Boundary Hazards* highlight the vulnerabilities of organisational boundaries. Technology often exposes organisations to the propagation of hazards across organisational boundaries. Moreover, the risk lays also in the shift of responsibilities across organisational boundaries and in the raising of mistrust across divisions of labour.
2. *Evolutionary Hazards* emerge in a lack of understanding of technology trajectories as results of social shaping of technology.
3. *Performativity Hazards* highlight how social connectivities (or social networks) extend technology and expose organisations to emerging hazards (e.g. negative feedback and imitation behaviour), which could contribute towards hardening social links and establishing hard homogeneous communities reducing diversity and structural resilience.

Fig. 6.1 Tensions of
socio-technical hazards

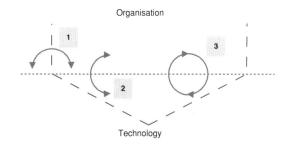

These classes of socio-technical hazards, complementing current risk assessment methodologies, allow a characterisation of emerging technological risk in complex organisational settings. The identified classes of socio-technical hazards provide, that is, underpin, a characterisation of the risk of technology innovation. The findings extend, that is, complement technology-driven risk analysis. Figure 6.1 shows a representation of the manifestations of the three classes of socio-technical hazards as tensions (or propagation directions) between organisation and technology [1].

Emerging technological risk, expressed in terms of *Boundary Hazards*, *Evolutionary Hazards* and *Performativity Hazards*, enhances our understanding of technology innovation. It allows us to analyse the risk involved with technology innovation. This complements and extends technology risk analysis. A lack of understanding of the basic mechanisms inhibits and undermines technology innovation. Moreover, it exposes organisations to technology risk. This manifests, for instance, as weak organisational knowledge or problematic technology interaction. The underpinning of emerging technological risk enhances our understanding of how basic socio-technical mechanisms expose organisations to socio-technical hazards. This provides new insights and understandings of emerging technological risk. The better our understanding of emerging technological risk, the better our ability to deploy technology enabling communities of practice, hence, *hardening social links*. However, it is necessary to understand how technology innovation exposes organisations to new classes of socio-technical hazards. On the other hand, social aspects of technology expose the limitations of pure technological dependability arguments. The studies of the underlying mechanisms draw some general lessons for understanding and addressing emerging technological risk. In conclusion, our account of technology risk identifies *new* classes of socio-technical hazards. The combination of these hazards together with the diverse risk accounts identifies a framework that enhances microscopic and macroscopic levels of risk analysis.

References

1. Anderson S, Felici M (2009) Classes of socio-technical hazards: microscopic and macroscopic scales of risk analysis. Risk Manag 11(34):208–240. doi:10.1057/rm.2009.7
2. Beck U (1992) Risk Society: Towards a New Modernity. Sage, London

3. Douglas M, Wildavsky A (1982) Risk and culture: an essay on the selection of technological and environmental dangers. University of California Press, Berkeley
4. Felici M (2006) Capturing emerging complex interactions: safety analysis in air traffic management. Reliab Eng Syst Saf 91(12):1482–1493. doi:10.1016/j.ress.2006.01.010
5. Le Coze J (2005) Are organisations too complex to be integrated in the technical risk assessment and current safety auditing? Saf Sci 43(8):613–638. doi:10.1016/j.ssci.2005.06.005
6. Le Coze J (2008) Disasters and organisations: from lessons learnt to theorising. Saf Sci 46(1):132–149. doi:10.1016/j.ssci.2006.12.001
7. MacKenzie D (2001) Physics and finance: S-terms and modern finance as a topic for science studies. Sci Technol Hum Values 26(2):115–144. doi:10.1177/016224390102600201
8. MacKenzie D (2003) An equation and its worlds: bricolage, exemplars, disunity and performativity in financial economics. Soc Stud Sci 33(6):831–868. doi:10.1177/0306312703336002
9. MacKenzie D (2003) Long-term capital management and the sociology of arbitrage. Econ Soc 32(3):349–380. doi:10.1080/03085140303130
10. MacKenzie D (2004) The big, bad wolf and the rational market: portfolio insurance, the 1987 crash and the performativity of economics. Econ Soc 33(3):303–334. doi:10.1080/0308514042000225680
11. MacKenzie D (2004) Social connectivities in global financial markets. Environ Plan D Soc Space 22(1):83–101. doi:10.1068/d317t
12. MacKenzie D, Millo Y (2003) Constructing a market, performing theory: the historical sociology of a financial derivatives exchange. Am J Sociol 109(1):107–145. doi:10.1086/374404
13. Neumann PG (1995) Computer related risks. ACM Press, New York
14. Perrow C (1999) Normal accidents: living with high-risk technologies. Princeton University Press, New Jersey

Annotated Bibliography

This annotated bibliography is intended to support researchers and professionals who would like to acquire a comprehensive view of *emerging technological risk*. The cited literature identifies a core set of knowledge that has been enhanced by our research and related to other relevant work. The result is a guided introduction to the complexity of technological risk. The literature in this annotated bibliography has driven discussions and debates within the *Interdisciplinary Research Collaboration in Dependability*—the DIRC project—hence, the *DIRC Risk Reader*.

1. Ackerman MS, Halverson CA. Reexamining organizational memory. *Commun ACM*, 43(1):59–64, January 2000.

   The analysis of procedures in contexts of use allows the characterisation of organisational memories. The empirical analysis of contexts of use highlights theoretical mechanisms underlying organisational memory. This allows the characterisation of organisational memory as distributed cognition. *Boundary Objects*, as artifacts, represent repositories of organisational memory. In order to enable organisational memory, it is necessary to understand the processes that make boundary objects available for reuse. Processes of *decontextualisation* and *recontextualisation* are necessary in order to activate boundary objects as organisational memories. Decontextualisation generalises boundary objects in such a way as to make them reusable in a different situation. Recontextualisation makes boundary objects usable for a specific situation. These processes allow the characterisation of organisational memory mechanisms in terms of boundary objects.

2. Ackerman MS, Halverson CA. Organizational memory as objects, processes, and trajectories: An examination of organizational memory in use. *Comput Support Coop Work*, 13(2):155–189, 2004.

   The paper revises and explains *organisational memory* in terms of distributed cognition. It presents a macro-analysis of a working activity. The analysis highlights the nature of organisational memory as distributed cognition

S. Anderson and M. Felici, *Emerging Technological Risk*,
DOI: 10.1007/978-1-4471-2143-5, © Springer-Verlag London Limited 2012

processes, which rely on and use various artifacts, or boundary objects. Boundary objects, on the one hand, represent repositories, on the other hand, enable processes of organisational memory. The trajectory of the representational states (in terms of boundary objects) captures work practices. The paper also points out that boundary objects as knowledge repositories are effective, if processes of contextualisation, decontextualisation and recontextualisation are in place. These processes, moreover, allow communities of practice to share (shape) boundary objects, enable organisational memory and make it available for reuse.

3. Adam B, Beck U, Van Loon J, editors. *The Risk Society and Beyond: Critical Issues for Social Theory*. SAGE Publications, 2000.

The collection discusses the role of social theory with respect to the *Risk Society*. On the one hand, it analyses how the Risk Society poses new problems to social theory. On the other hand, it questions how social theory understands the Risk Society. The discussion draws an understanding of the Risk Society with respect to social theory.

4. Alberdi E, Povyakalo A, Strigini L, Ayton P. Effects of incorrect computer-aided detection (CAD) output on human decision making in mammography. *Acad Radiol*, 11(8):909–918, 2004.

The paper investigates the effect of computer-aided detection on human decision making. It discusses trials drawn from the evaluation of a Computer-Aided Detection (CAD) tool developed for supporting mammography screening. The paper reports the results of two additional studies that were conducted in order to assess how CAD tools affect the *sensitivity* (i.e. proportion of recalled cancers) and *specificity* (i.e. proportion of normal cases that are not-recalled) of human film-readers. The results highlight contingencies in the assumption that *CAD increases the sensitivity of less qualified readers without adversely affecting their specificity*. The paper, finally, discusses the implication of how understanding the limitations of automation, i.e. how technical systems fail may influence overall performance of human-computer interaction in decision making.

5. Alberdi E, Povyakalo AA, Strigini L, Ayton P, Hartswood M, Procter R, Slack R. Use of computer-aided detection (CAD) tools in screening mammography: a multidisciplinary investigation. *Br J Radiol*, 78:S31–40, 2005.

The paper reports a study to assess the effect of Computer-Aided Detection (CAD) tools on screening mammograms. The underlying assumption of the adoption of a CAD tool is that it increases the sensitivity of readers (i.e. the proportion of cancers that are recalled for further assessment) without decreasing their specificity (i.e. the proportion of normal cases that are not recalled). The paper reports a multidisciplinary investigation consisting of statistical analyses (grounded in reliability modelling in engineering), experimental studies of screening mammograms and ethnographic observations. The analysis provides new insights on the assessment of reliability of heterogeneous systems (involving human-machine interaction) and on system usage. Moreover, the investigation points out that the adoption of CAD tools may have potentially detrimental effects (i.e. a decreased sensitivity) on particularly difficult cases. It provides results highlighting dependability issues relevant to advisory systems, in particular, used to support screening of mammograms.

6. Anderson R. Why information security is hard—an economic perspective. In *Proceedings of the 17th Annual Computer Security Applications Conference, ACSAC 2001*, pages 358–365. IEEE Computer Society, 2001.

The paper analyses information security from an economic perspective. It argues that an economic perspective, rather than a technological one, provides new insights in understanding computer security (mechanisms). In particular, it analyses how computer security mechanisms find explanation in important features of network economics (i.e. network externalities). It provides various examples that stress important features of information security technology markets.

7. Anderson R, Moore T. The Economics of Information Security. *Sci*, 314(5799): 610–613, October 2006.

The paper discusses how misaligned incentives may affect security. It discusses several examples, analyses security threats, and points out how vulnerabilities are giving rise to emergent markets for technologies. It advocates system design to be driven by principles drawn from the economics of information security. Finally, its concluding remarks generalise the insights and point towards similar arguments for the economics of dependability.

8. Anderson R, Moore T. The economics of information security: A survey and open questions. In *Proceedings of the Fourth bi-annual Conference on the Economics of the Software and Internet Industries*, 2007.

This paper discusses the *economics of information security*. In particular, it argues that economics theory provides an explanation to some vulnerabilities in information security. The paper draws similarities between research in economics and information security. It describes the basic concepts (e.g. positive and negative externalities) that underlie the economics of information security. The paper also reviews relevant literature, which highlights some aspects of information security. For instance, it discusses emerging "markets of vulnerabilities" and the incentives for security mechanisms. Moreover, it highlights how network security depends, to a certain extent, on individual behaviour (e.g. selfish users). Finally, the paper identifies three major research areas: (1) the design of "strategy-proof" mechanisms in order to take into account incentives, (2) the socio-technical study of emerging "network topology", and (3) the analysis of the "economics of dependability".

9. Anderson RJ. *Security Engineering: A Guide to Building Dependable Distributed Systems*. Wiley Publishing, second edition, 2008.

   The book identifies principles underlying security engineering. It reviews various security mechanisms and relevant design aspects. The book highlights design issues related to system security. It stresses how security is a complex feature. Unfortunately, many security mechanisms present subtle vulnerabilities. The book provides a starting point to understand security for complex systems.

10. Anderson S, Felici M. Requirements evolution—from process to product oriented management. In Bomarius F, Komi-Sirviö S, editors, *Proceedings of the Third International Conference on Product Focused Software Process Improvement, PROFES 2001*, number 2188 in LNCS, pages 27–41. Springer-Verlag, 2001.

    Requirements Evolution represents one of the major problems in developing computer-based systems. Current practice in Requirements Engineering relies on process-oriented methodologies, which lack product features. The resulting scenario then is a collection of general methodologies, which do not take into account product features that may enhance our ability in monitoring and controlling Requirements Evolution. The paper shows empirical investigations of two industrial case studies. The results point out evolutionary product features and identify an Empirical Framework for analysing Requirements Evolution. The work represents a shift from process to product-oriented management of Requirements Evolution.

11. Anderson S, Felici M. Quantitative aspects of requirements evolution. In *Proceedings of the 26th Annual International Conference on Computer Software and Applications Conference, COMPSAC 2002*, pages 27–32. IEEE Computer Society, August 2002.

    The paper investigates our ability to understand requirements evolution by means of metrics. The empirical investigation of an avionics industrial safety-critical case study assesses our ability to monitor requirements evolution by evolutionary trends and the *Requirements Maturity Index* (RMI). The paper proposes the *Historical Requirements Maturity Index* (HRMI), an enrichment of the RMI, in order to take into account process aspects and history of changes. The empirical results support the models underlying the proposed metrics. The empirical analysis of requirements evolution provides practical experience of measuring evolutionary information. Industry collects data which needs analysis from a life cycle and evolutionary perspective. The analysis of evolutionary information should always be carefully studied and understood within the specific industrial context. The empirical analysis provides an experience of how difficult it is effectively to apply even simple metrics in practice. The empirical nature of the work allows the experiment to be replicated in other industrial contexts.

12. Anderson S, Felici M. Classes of socio-technical hazards: Microscopic and macroscopic scales of risk analysis. *Risk Manag*, 11(3–4):208–240, 2009.

    The paper summarises and distills together multidisciplinary perspectives of technology risk in order to identify and define three classes of socio-technical hazards: *Boundary Hazards*, *Evolutionary Hazards* and *Performativity Hazards*. These classes enhance our understanding of technology risk. They highlight how diverse accounts of risk refer to different granularities of risk— (technological) microscopic and (organisational) macroscopic levels of risk analysis. The benefit of understanding and capturing socio-technical accounts of risk is twofold. On the one hand, it points toward an interdisciplinary account of technology risk. On the other hand, it provides a means for structuring risk analysis according to multidisciplinary perspectives. The combination of different levels of risk analysis enhances our understanding of the risk of technology innovation with respect to classes of socio-technical hazards.

13. Anderson S, Hardstone G, Procter R, Williams R. Down in the (data)base(ment): Supporting configuration in organisational information systems. In Ackerman MS, Halverson CA, Erickson T, Kellogg WA, editors, *Resources, Co-Evolution, and Artifacts: Theory in CSCW*, Comput Supported Coop Work, pages 221–253. Springer, 2008.

    The paper presents a case study for the introduction of a new organization-wide information system in the Healthcare domain. The new information system is central to the organisational objectives. Ethnographic studies highlight problems of coping with evolving classifications of work practices. The responses of users and of the project team to these problems have important implications for the usability and thus dependability of information infrastructures and the information they contain. Drawing insights from sociological studies of classification and standardisation the paper reflects upon the implications for the development and implementation of dependable information infrastructures.

14. Anderson S, Koornneef F, Voges U. Risk management for medical devices. *Phys Medica*, 19, 2003.

    The paper questions risk management for medical devices as regulated by the standards EN 1441 and ISO/IEC 14971, which assign responsibilities primarily on the manufacturers. The ISO/IEC 14971 addresses to some extent trade-offs between medical benefits and risk associated with medical devices. The paper points out that medical devices require a revised and extended approach to risk management. In particular, the paper highlights limitations of current approaches relevant to risk management for medical devices and discusses features (e.g. managing risk across organisational boundaries) addressing such limitations.

15. Arlat J, Blanquart J-P, Costes A, Crouzet Y, Deswarte Y, Fabre J-C, Guillermain H, Kaâniche M, Kanoun K, Laprie J-C, Mazet C, Powell D,

Rabéjac C, Thévenod P. Dependability Handbook. Technical Report 98-346, LAAS, 1998.

The technical report provides a comprehensive account of dependability methodologies drawn from research and practice on *fault tolerance* for safety-critical systems. It defines the basic concepts and terminology for dependability. An important aspect to be noted is that human-machine interactions and human adaptability are central aspects of dependability. This stresses the importance of assessing contingencies between 'human errors' and dependability. The report describes the basic concepts of dependability and the means for dependability. It highlights methodologies that contribute towards the design of dependable systems.

16. Atkinson C, Eldabi T, Paul RJ, Pouloudi A. Investigating integrated socio-technical approaches to health informatics. In *Proceedings of the 34th Hawaii International Conference on System Sciences*, pages 1–10. IEEE Computer Society, 2001.

The paper proposes and investigates the integration of different socio-technical approaches in order to deal with emerging issues in the domain of Health Informatics. The proposed integration involves three different approaches dealing with different aspects, i.e. information systems and technologies, participative simulation modelling, and stakeholder representation and analysis, concerning information systems in Healthcare. The paper discusses a rationale supporting socio-technical approaches for Health Informatics.

17. Aven T, Kristensen V. Perspectives on risk: review and discussion of the basis for establishing a unified and holistic approach. *Reliab Eng Syst Saf*, 90(1):1–14, 2005.

The paper considers and reviews diverse perspectives (e.g. engineering, economic and social) on risk. The diverse accounts of risk would benefit and complement each other. It then uses these perspectives in order to analyse three case studies. It stresses the usefulness of analysing different perspectives. It advocates that taking into account different risk perspectives provides the basis for a unified and holistic approach for risk assessment.

18. Avižienis A, Laprie J-C, Randell B, Landwehr C. Basic Concepts and Taxonomy of Dependable and Secure Computing. *IEEE Trans Dependable Secur Comput*, 1(1):11–33, January-March 2004.

The paper introduces the basic concepts of *dependability* and security. It revises the definition of system dependability—"the ability to deliver service that can justifiably be trusted"—to an alternative one: "the ability to avoid service failures that are more frequent and more severe that is acceptable". Basic attributes (i.e. *availability, reliability, safety, confidentiality, integrity* and *maintainability*) refine the notion of dependability. Note that security is defined in terms of availability, confidentiality and integrity. This relates security to dependability into an integrated framework. The basic definitions support the discussion of the main threats (i.e. *faults*, *errors* and *failures*) to dependability and security. The paper introduces the main means (i.e. *fault prevention*, *fault tolerance*, *fault removal* and *fault forecasting*) to achieve dependability and security. All definitions and concepts form a framework (tree) for dependability and security.

19. Baxter GD, Küster Filipe J, Miguel A, Tan K. The effects of timing and collaboration on dependability in the neonatal intensive care unit. In Redmill F, Anderson T, editors, *Constituents of modern system-safety thinking: Proceedings of the thirteenth safety-critical systems symposium*, pages 195–210. Springer-Verlag, 2005.

The paper analyses how timing and collaboration aspects contribute towards dependability. In particular, it analyses timing and collaboration within a *Neonatal Intensive Care Unit* (NICU). The analysis points out various timing aspects, which characterise different temporal interaction properties within the unit. Moreover, it highlights a hierarchical organisational structure guiding decision making processes. The discussion stresses how timing and interaction critically contribute towards knowledge (re)distribution within the unit. Timely knowledge is crucial for the overall dependability. The analysis is informative in order to gather requirements and operational aspects for a monitoring and decision support system.

20. Baxter GD, Monk AF, Tan K, Dear PRF, Newell SJ. Using cognitive tack analysis to facilitate the integration of decision support systems into the neonatal intensive care unit. *Artif Intell Med*, 35(3):243–257, 2005.

The paper is concerned with gathering (acceptability) requirements for an expert system to be developed and deployed in order to support decision making processes within a *Neonatal Intensive Care Unit* (NICU). It reports the results of a cognitive task analysis, which consists of a work context analysis by means of lightweight rich picture representations—a Critical Decision Method (CDM)—that highlights decision making processes. The task analysis points out the rich interaction of clinical staff. This interaction involves formal (e.g. meetings and ward rounds) as well as informal communications, various paper-based documents and technological interactions. The rich communication supports knowledge exchange and enables hierarchical decision making. The paper reports on the observations of two clinical cases. It discusses observed alarms and actions taken. The paper identifies some implications for the development and deployment of the expert system. In particular, it stresses that the expert system has to comply with and support the communication within the NICU, without altering established hierarchical decision making processes and work practices.

21. Beck U. *Risk Society: Towards a New Modernity*. SAGE Publications, 1992.

The analysis of recent developments in western society highlights a shift towards the *Risk Society*. Modernisation processes characterising the industrial society highlight the mechanisms that underlie modern society. Nowadays society is the Risk Society, as distinct from the class society. Risks spread across social, cultural and organisational boundaries. Knowledge (about risk) creates and supports people awareness. Knowledge distribution and availability, therefore, empower dynamics of the Risk Society. The Risk Society stresses that the social and the technological aspects are inseparable in modern industrialised society. Analysing the risk involves understanding how modernisation relates to sociality. This is captured by the concept of *reflexive modernisation*, which stresses how industrial processes have changed the relationships between social organisations and risks. Social, cultural and political hazards are then strongly related to technological hazards. The book introduces and defines the Risk Society as a paradigm for analysing the modern industrialised society.

22. Beck U, Bonss W, Lau C. The theory of reflexive modernization: Problematic, hypotheses and research programme. *Theory Cult Soc*, 20(2):1–33, 2003.

The paper questions the theory of *reflexive modernisation*. In particular, it discusses how "reflexivity in reflexive modernisation" highlights "the modernisation of the modern society". That is, the principles that characterise the modern society are now being institutionalised into the reflexive or "second modern society". The same principles being at the basis of the modern society now undermine its existence. The developments of the modern society question the foundations of the modern society itself. In particular, the distinction between modern and reflexive societies, although the segmentation is a useful simplification for the analysis, is evident in the boundaries. On the one hand, the modern society institutionalises the existence of various boundaries (e.g. social boundaries, national boundaries) as being fixed. On the other hand, the reflexive society questions these boundaries and considers them as inappropriate to deal with complex issues (e.g. environmental, ethical). Similarly, the theory of reflexive modernisation questions the nature of knowledge as soon as the boundaries are diluted and *uncertainties* or *side-effects* arise. The paper allows us to analyse and understand the struggles being currently experienced by various societies (e.g. information society, industrialised society) moving from the modern to the reflexive society.

23. Bernstein T. 'A grand success'. *IEEE Spectrum*, 10(2):54–58, February 1973.

The paper is an example of how technological innovation like the introduction of alternating current might be argued from a risk perspective. The point is that technological innovation might be argued by the discussion of related risk. However, people would have different perspectives about the risk associated with technological innovation. They would also discuss how technology risk might affect a particular class of people. The discussion, characterised by arguments and counter arguments, would involve different viewpoints associated to individual or societal interests.

24. Besnard D, Greathead D, Baxter G. When mental models go wrong: co-occurrences in dynamic, critical systems. *Int J Hum-Comput Stud*, 60(1):117–128, January 2004.

The paper analyses how the occurrence of events affects mental models. In particular, it investigates how consecutive events may reinforce some mental models and create dangerous conditions. The paper analyses situations drawn from an accident involving a commercial air crash. It draws some conclusions and implications for system design.

25. Bishop P, Bloomfield R, Clement C, Guerra S. Software criticality analysis of COTS/SOUP. *Reliab Eng Syst Saf*, 81(3):291–301, 2003.

The paper describes a *Software Criticality Analysis* (SCA) developed in order to support the use of Commercial-Off-The-Shelf (COTS) software in safety-related systems. The SCA methodology aims to assess the extent to which each component contributes to the safety of the whole system. The SCA methodology furthermore points out segregation between software components with different safety importance. The methodology consists of a combination of HAZOP analyses based on design documents and software inspections. The results point out that the assessment based only on architecture and design document would have been misleading.

26. Bishop P, Bloomfield R, Clement T, Guerra S. Software Criticality Analysis of COTS/SOUP. In Anderson S, Bologna S, Felici M, editors, *Proceedings of the 21st International Conference on Computer Safety, Reliability and Security, SAFECOMP 2002*, number 2434 in LNCS, pages 198–211. Springer-Verlag, 2002.

Commercial-Off-The-Shelf (COTS) solutions often provide readily available general software artifacts to be adopted in specific contexts. On the other hand, the adoption of COTS in safety critical domains requires suitable justifications and arguments. The paper proposes a Software Criticality Analysis (SCA) in order to classify software parts according to a Safety Critical Index (SCI). The SCI is directly related to the Safety Integrity Level (SIL) of the safety function the software contributes to. The SCA experience shows that safety assessment would benefit from additional information capturing subtle system interactions (e.g. system dependencies) as well as domain knowledge (e.g. expert judgement).

27. Bishop P, Bloomfield R, Clement T, Guerra S, Jones C. Integrity Static Analysis of COTS/SOUP. In Anderson S, Felici M, Littlewood B, editors, *Proceedings of the 22nd International Conference on Computer Safety, Reliability and Security, SAFECOMP 2003*, number 2788 in LNCS, pages 63–76. Springer-Verlag, 2003.

The paper presents an Integrity Static Analysis of COTS/SOUP (Commercial-Off-The-Shelf/Software-Of-Uncertain-Pedigree) software. The analysis consists of a combination of different tools and manual investigations.

It investigates the usage and presence of unsafe language constructs and covert flows. The former identifies issues with known problems of programming styles for safety-critical domains. The latter highlights potential hazards of dependencies between different software parts. The analysis contributes towards the construction of supportive arguments for the use and adoption of COTS/SOUP software in safety-critical domains. The paper reports the experience and results of adopting the proposed analysis for software consisting of C and assembler programs.

28. Bloomfield R, Littlewood B. Multi-legged arguments: the impact of diversity upon confidence in dependability arguments. In *Proceedings of the 2003 International Conference on Dependable Systems and Networks, DSN'03*, pages 25–34. IEEE Computer Society, 2003.

The use of diverse arguments, or multi-legged arguments, is intended to increase our confidence in dependability claims or safety cases. The paper highlights similarities and differences between diversity in design and diversity in arguments. Although the use of diversity in arguments should intuitively increase our confidence in dependability claims, the paper points out contingencies between the independence or dependency between arguments. The probabilistic characterisation of the problem identifies issues with dependency in multi-legged arguments and provides new insights for future research on the compositionality of multi-legged arguments.

29. Bloomfield R, Littlewood B. On the use of diverse arguments to increase confidence in dependability claims. In Besnard D, Gacek C, Jones CB, editors, *Structure for Dependability: Computer-Based Systems from an Interdisciplinary Perspective*, chapter 13, pages 254–268. Springer-Verlag, 2006.

Multi-legged (or diversity) arguments allow us to acquire confidence in dependability claims. The combination of different and diverse arguments presents contingencies due to dependencies. It is possible to identify sources of uncertainty for dependability claims. An analytical characterisation points out two main sources of uncertainty: doubt about underpinning assumptions and weakness of evidence. The formalisation of these subtle uncertainties highlights pitfalls in multi-legged arguments. In particular, there could be cases in which an argument (e.g. a statistical argument) undermines the assumptions underlying another argument of a different type (e.g. a logical argument).

30. Blythe M, Monk A. Net neighbours: adapting HCI methods to cross the digital divide. *Interact Comput*, 17(1):35–56, 2005.

The paper reports the development of a service, named Net Neighbours, that provides accessibility to an online shopping scheme for older people or people with disabilities. The paper describes the adopted process for gathering the requirements and identifying potential hazards. The development process relies on Human-Computer Interaction methodologies. The paper stresses the possibility of providing technological services, such as online shopping, by supporting social relationships. This extends technology mediated communities and allows people to use services that they would otherwise have been excluded from due to social, cultural and technological barriers. The paper highlights some hazards (e.g. trust, security, privacy) to which people are exposed through socially and technologically mediated relationships.

31. Blythe MA, Monk AF, Doughty K. Socially dependable design: The challenge of ageing population for HCI. *Interact Comput*, 17(6):672–689, 2005.

The paper discusses how ageing populations pose particular challenges for Human-Computer Interaction design. In particular, the paper is concerned with hazards and risks for ageing populations. It discusses how technology can assist older or elderly people, although it needs to address relevant design issues. It draws over ethnographic studies and statistics in order to derive requirements for such technology. The paper highlights particular hazards concerning relevant social issues for ageing populations. It advocates *socially dependable design* in order to address emerging hazards. It argues that technology, in such contexts, is often used as a means for maintaining social networks and reducing social isolation. It stresses that technology exposes people to emerging social hazards, rather than purely technological ones: "A design that has the potential to stigmatise its user is reinforcing a particular view of the place of older people in society." The paper questions how technology (design) takes into account *responsibility* and *privacy* requirements. It points out how system usage giving rise to *false allarms* allows people to maintain social awareness. It advocates inclusive design in order to make technology available to a wide community and to reduce the cost barrier. The paper argues *socially dependable systems* take account of the social contexts and support social accessibility.

32. Borodzicz EP. *Risk, Crisis & Security Management*. John Wiley & Sons, 2005.

The book provides an account of risk in relation to crisis and security management. It emphasises risk, crisis and security management from an organisational viewpoint. It introduces the use of simulations and games as a means for training and crisis management. It discusses risks and security management issues that concern complex accidents or events (e.g. September 11th and City University's recovery from fire).

33. Bottitta S, Felici M. Understanding and learning trust: A review, characterization and tool. In Guedes Soares C, Zio E, editors, *Safety and Reliability for Managing Risk, Proceedings of the European Safety and Reliability Conference 2006, ESREL 2006*, volume 2, pages 1273–1280. Taylor & Francis Group, 2006.

A review highlights multidisciplinary aspects of trust. Trust games as extensions of the *Prisoner's Dilemma* allow us to study and analyse trust dynamics. They capture those situations in which cooperation (or competition) between two entities arises. It is necessary to investigate different trust strategies, dynamics and their interactions (e.g. trust formation). The paper describes a proof-of-concept tool for trust games. The tool represents trust games graphically. It supports analysing alternative trust scenarios and their results.

34. Bowker GC. The history of information infrastructures: The case of the international classification of diseases. *Inf Process Manag*, 32(1):49–61, 1996.

   The paper analyses the historical developments of the *International Classification of Diseases* (ICD), nowadays maintained by the *World Health Organization* (WHO) and adopted worldwide. The history of the ICD, as information infrastructure, is related to the development of the *"modern state"*, which seeks a means for classifying and monitoring societal developments (like diseases) with the aim of controlling them. On the one hand, it is possible to analyse the socio-cultural-political accounts reflected or embedded into the ICD. On the other hand, the history of the ICD is related to modern developments of information technologies, which have affected the ICD as well as the bureaucracies and information gathering practices. The ICD provides an example of the tight relationships between information infrastructures, technologies and communities of practice.

35. Bowker GC, Star SL. Building Information Infrastructures for Social Worlds—The Role of Classifications and Standards. In Ishida T, editor, *Community Computing and Support Systems*, number 1519 in LNCS, pages 231–248. Springer-Verlag, 1998.

   The paper analyses aspects of classifications and standards that are relevant in the building of information infrastructures. In particular, it analyses properties of classifications (standards) and identifies two analytic dimensions *space* and *time*, respectively. The space dimension takes into account Actor-Network Theory (ANT) in order to analyse the *ubiquity*—i.e. the presence of classifications (standards)— and the *material texture*—i.e. the objectivity of classifying and standardising—of classifications (standards). The time dimension analyses how classifications (standards) enable historical reconstructing and organisational memory (forgetting). Combining these two dimensions enables capturing political debates of different communities who have been forging classifications (standards). The paper analyses these aspects by investigating a case study drawn from the building of an information infrastructure for a *Nursing Intervention Classification* (NIC) system.

36. Bowker GC, Star SL. *Sorting Things Out: Classification and its Consequences*. The MIT Press, 1999.

   Classifications as *Information Infrastructures* enable cooperation between different *communities of practice*. It is possible to analyse classifications in terms of *Boundary Objects* as resulting from the social and political mediation between different communities of practice. Looking at classifications as resulting from mediation of social and political communities allows the analysis of Information Infrastructures and Boundary Objects. The analysis emphasises the crucial role of classifications in enabling work practice as well as communication and cooperation between different communities. It is possible, therefore, to analyse classifications as results of complex socio-technical relationships (e.g. social networks mapping boundary objects and standards). This highlights the evolutionary nature of classifications—"The only good classification is a living classification".

37. Bruseberg A. The design of complete systems: Providing human factors guidance for COTS acquisition. *Reliab Eng Syst Saf*, 91(12):1554–1565, December 2006.

The paper discusses the need for guidance in assessing human factors, both hazards and benefits, for the acquisition of Commercial-Off-The-Shelf (COTS) equipment. Economical drivers often advocate the adoption of COTS systems (e.g. software, hardware) with little consideration for human factors. Unfortunately, the COTS design life cycle provides limited opportunity for customisations and local adaptations, therefore, it is necessary to support the selection and acquisition processes by taking into account human factors too. The paper stresses the need to identify general guidelines, which support early assessment and decision-making for management. It presents and discusses a general questionnaire for the assessment of human factors for COTS products. The questionnaire provides a means for the identification and communication of human factors across domains. The generality of the questionnaire intends to support human factors assessment by non-experts (in human factors) at the early stages of the selection and acquisition processes. The paper draws on the experience of using the questionnaire in a military domain.

38. Büscher M, Shapiro D, Hartswood M, Procter R, Slack R, Voß A, Mogensen P. Promises, premises and risks: Sharing responsibilities, working up trust and sustaining commitment in participatory design projects. In Binder T, Gregory J, Wagner I, editors, *Proceedings of the Participatory Design Conference, PDC 2002*, pages 183–192, June 2002.

The paper highlights how co-realisation facilitates trust in technology innovation. It enables mechanisms for sharing and clearly defining responsibilities between technology designers and users. Trust between technology designers and users mitigates risk perception and enables exploratory approaches to technology innovation. The paper reports four different case studies that highlight benefits and limitations of co-realisation with respect to technology innovation.

39. Busse DK, Holland B. Implementation of Critical Incident Reporting in a Neonatal Intensive Care Unit. *Cogn Technol Work*, 4(2):101–106, 2002.

The paper reports an experience in implementing a *critical incident reporting scheme* in a *Neonatal Intensive Care Unit* (NICU). Incident reporting schemes aim, in general, at providing feedback to organisations in order to address failures. The paper stresses the need for adopting reporting schemes in medical domains similar to the ones applied in other industries (e.g. avionics or chemical). The issues arising emphasise how the classification underlying the reporting scheme is crucial in order to avoid the stigmatisation of failures as *'human errors'*. Moreover, it stresses that the reporting scheme, in order to be effective, needs to capture local conditions and requirements as well as a *meaningful classification*.

40. Cheverst K, Clarke K, Dewsbury G, Hemmings T, Kember S, Rodden T, Rouncefield M. Designing assistive technologies for medication regimes in care settings. *Univers Access Inf Soc*, 2(3):235–242, 2003.

    The paper presents preliminary investigations of requirements gathering and design for assistive technology. In particular, the paper is concerned with the design and deployment of technology that might expose vulnerable people (e.g. former psychiatric patients) to hazards. The paper highlights that technology design and innovation need to take account of the rich social interactions characterising particular application domains. It reports several concerns that arose in the fieldwork. Firstly, it is clear that technology artifacts may shift or redistribute responsibilities. This shift may undermine the use of technology intended to support medication regimes exposing people to overdosing or mistreatment (e.g. forgetting medicine). Secondly, technology deployments need to take account of work practices and patient trajectories. A lack of understanding of these aspects may result in timing or treatment issues. Early results emphasise that it is important to understand cultural and organisational aspects in order to deploy technology innovation successfully and to enable specific user groups.

41. Churchill EF, Halverson CA. Social networks and social networking: Guest editors' introduction. *IEEE Internet Comput*, 9(5):14–19, 2005.

    The paper provides a brief introduction to (a special issue on) research in *Social Networks* and *Social Networking*. It highlights origins of social network theories. In particular, it provides a background on *Social Network Analysis (SNA)*, which relies on the representation of social networks by *sociograms*. Sociograms, as representation of social networks, consist of social entities and the connections among them. Properties and changing patterns of social networks inform the design of technology. The paper also provides pointers to relevant literature and resources (e.g. tools).

42. Civil Aviation Authority. *CAP 719—Fundamental Human Factor Concepts*, February 2002.

    The document stresses the importance of human factors for the aviation industry. In particular, it refers to the SHEL (Software, Hardware, Environment and Liveware) model as a conceptual model for human factors. The SHEL model enables the discussion of concepts of human factors, which are relevant for the aviation industry.

43. Clarke K, Hartswood M, Procter R, Rouncefield M, Slack R. Trusting the record. *Methods Inf Med*, 42(4):345–352, 2003.

The paper presents an ethnographic study of work practice drawn from a toxicology ward within a hospital. It emphasises the role of paper-based records in supporting local work practices. Paper-based records represent an organisational account of conducted activities. Moreover, paper-based records as mediating artifacts enable, coordinate and support social interactions as well as knowledge gathering and redistribution. The paper argues that technology innovation involving the introduction of an Electronic Medical Record (EMR) needs to understand and support contingencies between work practices, social interactions and embedding knowledge in technological artifacts. The intrusiveness of technology may modify the balances, obtained over co-evolved practices and artifacts, giving rise to disruptive organisational feedback.

44. Clarke K, Hartswood M, Procter R, Rouncefield M, Slack R, Williams R. Improving 'knife to skin time': process modelling and new technology in medical work. *Health Informatics J*, 8(1):39–42, 2002.

The paper investigates process modelling in medical settings. It emphasises how process modelling is the result of negotiated and coordinated activities. As such, process maps are critical supports for work practice in achieving mutual relevance, awareness and coordination among communities. The paper draws on the investigations of medical settings. The findings highlight the role of process modelling (hence, process maps) in achieving dependable processes. It stresses that new technology needs to capture the underlying mechanisms of process modelling, which finds ground in contextualised (local) work practice. Therefore, it warns about contingencies in standardising and transferring process maps across organisational boundaries and into technology artifacts.

45. Clarke K, Hughes J, Martin D, Rouncefield M, Sommerville I, Voß A, Procter R, Slack R, Hartswood M. 'Its About Time': Temporal Features of Dependability. In Clarke K, Hardstone G, Rouncefield M, Sommerville I, editors, *Trust in Technology: A Socio-Technical Perspective*, volume 36 of *Comput Supported Coop Work*, chapter 4, pages 105–121. Springer, 2006.

The paper discusses time and timeliness aspects of dependability. It emphasises contingencies between dependability and timing. The paper builds on several case studies and highlights coupling between timing aspects and work practices. In particular, it points out how trajectories capture the interaction between timing aspects, knowledge and work practices. On the one hand, temporal rhythms order activities. On the other hand, they stress the availability of knowledge as being critical for the dependable termination of specific activities. It highlights how process modelling points out that mutual-relationship and coordination are important for sharing knowledge. The paper argues that the development of new technology and its introduction need to take into account how technology innovation modifies timing aspects of work practices. It is important to understand how technology is related to contingencies between timing and knowledge with respect to work practices.

46. Clarke K, Hughes J, Rouncefield M, Hemmings T. When a bed is not a bed: Calculation and calculability in complex organizational settings. In Clarke K, Hardstone G, Rouncefield M, Sommerville I, editors, *Trust in Technology: A Socio-Technical Perspective*, volume 36 of *Comput Supported Coop Work*, chapter 2, pages 21–38. Springer, 2006.

The paper presents results of an ethnographic study of bed management drawn from work practices in NHS (National Health Service) Hospitals. It points out contingencies in work practice of bed management. It shows how work practices are critical in interpreting and aligning artifacts, hence, global and local knowledge. What initially seems inefficient information management is localised understanding of calculations, as results of interpreting local knowledge, and calculability, as embedding work practices. The case study clearly highlights how global, as well as local, knowledge is related to work practices. The paper discusses the potential disruptiveness of technology innovation as a strategy for improving overall performances.

47. Clarke KM, Hartswood MJ, Procter RN, Rouncefield M. The electronic medical record and everyday medical work. *Health Informatics J*, 7(3–4):168–170, 2001.

The paper reports an ethnographic study of work practice drawn from a toxicology ward within a hospital. It highlights how work practices involve negotiation and interaction between professionals. Both cooperation and interaction contribute towards establishing a shared understanding, i.e. knowledge, about evolving patient trajectories. Cooperation and interaction rely on past experience and trust. Central to cooperation and interaction is the patient record, which acts as a boundary object mediated by work practice. The interpretation of the patient record, that is, understanding local knowledge, requires membership and awareness of organisational procedures and work practices. The paper questions whether or not the adoption of an Electronic Medical Record (EMR) for the sake of technology innovation will support local work practice. It argues that any strategy of technology innovation involving the introduction of an EMR has to take into account the mediating role of technological artifacts within organisational interaction and knowledge.

48. Constant EW II. Communities and hierarchies: structure in the practice of science and technology. In Laudan R, editor, *The Nature of technological knowledge: are models of scientific change relevant?* Kluwer, 1984.

The paper discusses a model that characterises the evolution of technology. The notions of "functional-failure" and "presumptive anomaly" are central to the characterisation of technological developments. The paper draws on a social analysis of the design and evolution of turbine systems. It emphasises a relationship between communities of practice, hierarchies and technological developments. The analysis discusses major differences and similarities between science and technology. Although science and technology may present some structural similarities, a "much closer attention to hierarchical structure, to modes of satisficing, and to social roles and context can greatly enrich the understanding of both enterprises."

49. Coulter N. ACM's computing classification system reflects changing times. *Commun ACM*, 40(12):111–112, 1997.

The paper discusses the 1998 ACM's Computing Classification System (CCS). The CCS is a classification system adopted by different groups and organisations for indexing, organising and interpreting relevant computing literature. The paper also describes recommendations for future updates of the classification system.

50. D'Adderio L. Crafting the virtual prototype: how firms integrate knowledge and capabilities across organisational boundaries. *Res Policy*, 30(9):1409–1424, 2001.

The investigations of case studies drawn from an industrial manufacturing domain highlights how software artifacts allow the integration of organisational knowledge. The transfer-of-knowledge into software artifacts involves processes of generalisations and contextualisations. These processes, moreover, enable the coordination and communication between different organisational units, or communities of practice (e.g. engineers and designers). Therefore, embedding organisational knowledge into software artifacts involves a coevolutionary process. On the one hand, knowledge acquisition and generalisation involve processes of codification and simplification. On the other hand, knowledge utilisation involves processes of reinstatement of subjectivity and local knowledge.

51. D'Adderio L. Configuring software, reconfiguring memories: the influence of integrated systems on knowledge storage, retrieval and reuse. In *Proceedings of the 2002 ACM Symposium on Applied Computing, SAC 2002*, pages 726–731. ACM, March 2002.

The paper questions innovation strategies adopting software systems in order to impose standardisation, hence decrease heterogeneity, across organisations. The investigation of a case study drawn from the automotive domain points out contingencies in adopting software systems as a means for capturing diverse organisational knowledge. The results highlight a paradox. Although the adoption of integrated technology intends to provide common organisational infrastructures, it allows diversities and contingencies across organisational boundaries and divisions of labour to emerge. The paper draws over the lessons learned and conclusions about dependability implications for organisations adopting software technology as a means to establish standardisation practice and to coordinate divisions of labour.

52. D'Adderio L. Configuring software, reconfiguring memories: the influence of integrated systems on the reproduction of knowledge and routines. *Ind Corp Chang*, 12(2):321–350, 2003.

The introduction of new software artifacts is often related to the need for integrating and coordinating different production activities within organisations. Although technological innovation involving software systems often promises further integration, coordination and efficiency, it requires a negotiation of knowledge distribution across the organisation. The analysis of the introduction of a software system (i.e. Product Data Manager) highlights how organisations need to reorganise work practices and knowledge distribution carefully. Software systems can enable and support declarative and procedural organisational memory.

53. D'Adderio L. *Inside the Virtual Product: How Organisations Create Knowledge Through Software*. Edward Elgar, 2003.

The book draws over a case study of a participant-observation at an automotive manufacturer. It investigates the epistemic implications for organisations adopting integrated software systems as coordination and standardisation strategies. Although technology innovation stresses the adoption of integrated software systems, they have subtle implications for adopting organisations. In particular, for instance, integrated information systems impact on the organisational ability in dealing with process changes and flexibilities. Moreover, contingencies arise across organisational boundaries and divisions of labour due to integration and standardisation objectives that reduce organisational resilience and diversity.

54. Dewsbury G, Sommerville I, Clarke K, Rouncefield M. A Dependability Model for Domestic Systems. In Anderson S, Felici M, Littlewood B, editors, *Proceedings of the 22nd International Conference on Computer Safety, Reliability, and Security, SAFECOMP 2003*, number 2788 in LNCS, pages 103–115. Springer-Verlag, 2003.

The paper proposes an extension to a dependability model, usually adopted for the assessment of systems comprising hardware and software. It reviews the basics of the dependability model and some of its underlying assumptions. It discusses some limitations of the dependability model with respect to *domestic systems*, in particular, *assistive technology* that intends to support elderly and disabled people. The paper highlights that assistive technology gives rise to user requirements that expose some limitations that concern dependability modelling.

55. Douglas M, Wildavsky A. *Risk and Culture: An Essay on the Selection of Technological and Environmental Dangers*. University of California Press, 1982.

Douglas and Wildavsky develop a *Cultural Theory* of risk and risk perception. They analyse the nature of risk and risk perception from a social viewpoint. Considering risk as result of a combination of *knowledge* and (public) *consent* allows the simplification and identification of four problems of risk. Each one of them is obtained by a combination of knowledge and consent. The four problems explain to some extent the nature of risk and risk management (e.g. risk assessment, risk classification). Douglas and Wildavsky's Cultural Theory allows the characterisation and generalisation of risk selection and risk perception. In *Risk and Culture*, Douglas and Wildavsky identify and analyse three different organisational societies (i.e. hierarchical, individualist and sectarian organisation societies). The underlying organisational structures, rules and values (analysed according to *grid/group theory*) show how social and cultural aspects bias or affect risk selection and perception.

56. Felici M. *Observational Models of Requirements Evolution*. PhD thesis, School of Informatics, University of Edinburgh, 2004.

The PhD thesis investigates an understanding of requirements evolution and explores new directions in requirements evolution research. Empirical analyses of industrial case studies highlight software requirements evolution as an important issue. Requirements, as mappings between socio-technical solutions and problems, represent an account of the history of socio-technical issues arising and being solved within industrial settings. The formal extension of a heterogeneous account of requirements provides a framework to model and capture requirements evolution. The application of the proposed framework provides further evidence that it is possible to capture and model evolutionary information about requirements. A discussion of scenarios of use stresses practical necessities for methodologies addressing requirements evolution. Finally, the identification of a broad spectrum of evolutions in socio-technical systems points out strong contingencies between system evolution and dependability. The PhD thesis argues that the better our understanding of socio-technical evolution, the better system dependability.

57. Felici M. Evolutionary Safety Analysis: Motivations from the Air Traffic Management Domain. In Winther R, Gran BA, Dahll G, editors, *Proceedings of the 24th International Conference on Computer Safety, Reliability and Security, SAFECOMP 2005*, number 3688 in LNCS, pages 208–221. Springer-Verlag, 2005.

In order realistically and cost-effectively to realise the ATM (Air Traffic Management) 2000+ Strategy, systems from different suppliers will be interconnected to form a complete functional and operational environment, covering ground segments and aerospace. This requires ATM services to go through significant structural, operational and cultural changes that will contribute towards the ATM 2000+ Strategy. Future ATM services will employ new systems forming an emergent ATM architecture underlying and supporting the European Commission's Single European Sky Initiative. Recent safety requirements, defined by EUROCONTROL (European organization for the safety of air navigation), imply the adoption of safety analysis for the introduction of new systems and their related procedures in the ATM domain.

Unfortunately, ATM systems and procedures have distinct characteristics (e.g. openness, volatility) that expose limitations of safety analyses. Although safety analysis stresses the assessment of evolving systems, it provides limited guidelines on how to cope with evolution in specific projects. The paper is concerned with problems in modelling ATM systems for safety analysis. It highlights a model specifically targeted to support evolutionary safety analysis.

58. Felici M. Capturing emerging complex interactions: Safety analysis in air traffic management. *Reliab Eng Syst Saf*, 91(12):1482–1493, 2006.

The paper shows an example of complex interaction drawn from the Air Traffic Management (ATM) domain. The ATM domain highlights how safety-critical activities rely on complex socio-technical interactions. The systemic reconstruction of an accident uses a representation that highlights the interactions among heterogeneous resources. The simple systemic reconstruction of the accident scenario points out two of the critical factors in the accident: timeliness and knowledge. Interactions are a means for enabling the (re)distribution of knowledge among heterogeneous actors and resources. The distribution of knowledge and its interaction strategies allow the characterisation of socio-technical interactions. These complex interactions expose the limitations of safety analyses. The paper introduces a framework, which addresses three main points in order effectively to support evolutionary safety analysis and to capture emerging complex interactions. Firstly, the model questions the system boundaries and the required level of details. The second point directly addresses unexpected complex interactions between system elements as the main source of incidents. The third characteristic of the model refers to the possibility of effective re-use of (part of) the model to inform future safety analyses. The framework supports evolutionary safety analysis.

59. Felici M. Modeling Safety Case Evolution—Examples from the Air Traffic Management Domain. In Guelfi N, Savidis A, editors, *Proceedings of the 2nd International Workshop on Rapid Integration of Software Engineering Techniques, RISE 2005*, number 3943 in LNCS, pages 81–96. Springer-Verlag, 2006.

The paper is concerned with evolutionary aspects in judging safety for ATM (Air Traffic Management) systems. The systematic production of safety analysis (models) will decrease the cost of conducting safety analysis by supporting reuse in future ATM projects. The paper introduces a logical framework for modelling and capturing safety case changes. Examples of safety case changes show how the framework enhances the understanding of safety case evolution. The formalisation of safety case changes and problems supports model-driven judgement. The formal framework highlights safety judgement (that is, the construction of safety cases) as an organisational process. That is, the safety judgement consists of gathering organisational knowledge about the system. This further highlights how organisational (knowledge) failures affect safety.

60. Felici M. Structuring evolution: on the evolution of socio-technical systems. In Besnard D, Gacek C, Jones C, editors, *Structure for Dependability: Computer-Based Systems from an Interdisciplinary Perspective*, chapter 3, pages 49–73. Springer, 2006.

Evolution is a complex phenomenon. On the one hand, evolution affects structures. On the other hand, structures support evolution too. Modelling evolution involves understanding how stakeholder interaction affects structure, that is, how structures capture stakeholder interaction. The work analyses mechanisms and examples of evolution of socio-technical structures (e.g. architecture, traceability, coupling, dependency), hence the *evolution of socio-technical systems*. It provides a formal characterisation of evolution for emerging structures in socio-technical systems. Capturing emerging structures (e.g. dependency) in socio-technical systems allows the (formal) modelling of evolutionary mechanisms, hence, the evolution of socio-technical systems. The identification of a broad spectrum of evolutions in socio-technical systems points out strong contingencies between system evolution and dependability.

61. Felici M. Trust strategies: Motivations from the Air Traffic Management domain. In Guedes Soares C, Zio E, editors, *Safety and Reliability for Managing Risk, Proceedings of the European Safety and Reliability Conference 2006, ESREL 2006*, volume 3, pages 1797–1804. Taylor & Francis Group, 2006.

Introducing safety relevant systems in Air Traffic Management (ATM) contexts requires us to understand the risk involved in order to mitigate the impact of possible failures. The paper is concerned with trust in technology. Although technology innovation supports further (e.g. safety or performance) improvements, there is often a lack of trust in changes. It argues that organisations need to identify trust strategies supporting the delivery of technology innovation. Moreover, the identification of strategies for building on trust supports the understating of subtle interactions between diverse, often competing, system objectives.

62. Felici M. Trust Strategies and Policies in Complex Socio-technical Safety-Critical Domains: An Analysis of the Air Traffic Management Domain. In Guelfi N, Buchs D, editors, *Proceedings of the 3rd International Workshop on Rapid Integration of Software Engineering techniques, RISE 2006*, number 4401 in LNCS, pages 51—65. Springer-Verlag, 2007.

Technology innovation supports further improvements, although there is often a lack of trust in changes. The paper is concerned with trust in technology. The analysis of trust with respect to risk perception and knowledge allows the characterisation of practical situations in which trust (or mistrust) emerges. It argues that organisations need to identify trust strategies and policies supporting the delivery of technology innovation. Moreover, the identification of trust strategies and policies supports the understanding of subtle interactions between diverse, often competing, system objectives. Trust strategies and

policies need to capture how socially constructed risk and knowledge (e.g.
system reliability) interact with each other. The paper stresses trust strategies
(in terms of game theory) and trust policies for the investigation of interaction
between trust, risk and knowledge.

63. Gigerenzer G. *Reckoning with Risk: Learning to Live with Uncertainty*.
Penguin Books, 2002.

Knowledge uncertainty relates to *risk*. The book examines risk as uncertainty
in terms of probabilities or frequencies based on empirical data. It highlights
miscommunication of risk in terms of probabilities (e.g. relative probabilities).
Case studies drawn from various domains (e.g. medical domain of breast
cancer screening) highlight how the representation of risk in terms of
probabilities (e.g. conditional probabilities or natural frequencies) affects its
perception and reasoning. The representation often favours miscommunication
of risk (e.g. in terms of relative rather than absolute risk). This is often due to
innumeracy with respect to probabilities. On the one hand, different groups of
people may use different reference classes (or classifications) giving rise to
uncertainty and miscommunication. On the other hand, they may exploit
ignorance of risk. Although some representations of risk are likely to favour
miscommunication, social and organisational factors (e.g. divisions of labour,
legal and financial incentive structures, conflicts of interest) inhibit work
practices like, for instance, *evidence-based medicine* (e.g. informed consent).
This stresses that risk perception depends on two main factors: *knowledge
representations* and *social aspects* (e.g. social structures). Both knowledge
(uncertainty) and social aspects affect risk perception.

64. Gigerenzer G, Todd PM, The ABC Research Group. *Simple Heuristics That
Make Us Smart*. Oxford University Press, 1999.

Bounded Rationality provides an alternative perspective to probabilistic
approaches of knowledge. Reasoning and decision-making processes often rely
on limited information and constrained environmental conditions.
Understanding bounded rationality allows the identification of fast and frugal
heuristics, which provide a characterisation of human reasoning and decision-
making in real situations exhibiting limited computational capacities and
resources. The analysis in situated cases identifies in fast and frugal heuristics
valuable tools for understanding processes of reasoning and decision-making
under constrained knowledge. The performance of fast and frugal heuristics
exhibits some sensitivity to information structure (or ecology), that is, how
information is distributed or organised in the environment.

65. Gurr C, Hardstone G. Implementing configurable information systems:
A combined social science and cognitive science approach. In Beynon M,
Nehaniv CL, Dautenhahn K, editors, *Proceedings of CT 2001*, number 2117 in
LNAI, pages 391–404. Springer-Verlag, 2001.

Diagrammatic representations can capture domain knowledge enabling the design of configurable information systems. The characterisation of organisational knowledge highlights social connectivities and artifacts as carriers. Diagrammatic representations allow the capturing of social networks as well as knowledge clusters. The use of diagrammatic representations, moreover, as a communication means allows the interaction and collaboration of stakeholders during design. Therefore, diagrammatic representations are enabling artifacts for communities of practices. The investigation of diagrammatic representations in use highlights how they capture domain specific knowledge informing system design and deployment.

66. Halverson CA. Activity Theory and Distributed Cognition: Or What Does CSCW Need to DO with Theories? *Comput Supported Coop Work*, 11(1–2): 243–267, 2002.

The paper compares *Activity Theory* and *Distributed Cognition* according to four important properties (i.e. *descriptive, rhetorical, inferential and application power*) in order to assess their contributions in the field of *Computer Supported Cooperative Work* (CSCW). Although they differently focus on the unit of analysis, both theories take account of cognitive processes. On the one hand, Activity Theory focuses on the performed activities and the negotiation within communities. On the other hand, Distributed Cognition captures cognitive processes involving interaction of people or diverse artifacts. Therefore, they enable analyses of cognitive processes at different levels of granularities. Unfortunately, both theories provide limited support in predicting, for instance, the impact (e.g. in terms of changes) of technology innovation. However, they provide suitable theories in order to analyse cognition processes like, for instance, how technology artifacts enable organisational memories and knowledge management activities. Although they support technology design differently, they both account for the social and cultural context of cognition.

67. Hardstone G, D'Adderio L, Williams R. Standardization, trust and dependability. In Clarke K, Hardstone G, Rouncefield M, Sommerville I, editors, *Trust in Technology: A Socio-Technical Perspective*, volume 36 of *Comput Supported Coop Work*, chapter 4, pages 69–103. Springer, 2006.

Standardisation of information systems intends to enhance overall visibility (e.g. in terms of analysis) and control over organisational activities. Moreover, standardisation is to enable communication and coordination between different communities of practices within an organisation or belonging to different organisations. The analysis of three different case studies points out the benefits as well as the drawbacks of standardisation practices. Social aspects of organisational knowledge in communities of practices expose the limitations of standardisation and identify in it a cause for lack of trust and undependability.

68. Hardstone G, Hartswood M, Procter R, Slack R, Voss A, Rees G. Supporting informality: Team working and integrated care records. In *Proceedings of the 2004 ACM conference on Computer Supported Cooperative Work, CSCW'04*, pages 142–151. ACM, 2004.

The paper reports an ethnographic study in the healthcare domain. The results emphasise the role of informal discussions and provisional judgements as part of work practices by which teams achieve agreements upon clinical management decisions over time. The paper highlights how paper-based documentation supports collaborative work by affording both the revision of preliminary clinical management options and the recognition of contributions by team members with different clinical perspectives and expertise. Finally, the paper considers the implications of introducing an Integrated Care Record (ICR) as clinical documentation becomes increasingly held and distributed electronically.

69. Hartswood M, Procter P, Slack R, Voß A, Büscher M, Rouncefield M, Rouchy P. Co-realisation: Towards a principled synthesis of ethnomethodology and participatory design. *Scand J Inf Syst*, 14(2):9–30, 2002.

Co-realisation articulates the basic principles of ethnography and participatory design into emerging technological artifacts. On the one hand, co-realisation acquires organisational knowledge by studying and learning work practices. On the other hand, co-realisation facilitates the deployment of technological innovation by contextualised design of technological artifacts. The paper presents two different case studies of co-realisation. The results highlight how co-realisation could be beneficial for engineering technological innovation.

70. Hartswood M, Procter R, Rouncefield M, Slack R. Performance management in breast screening: A case study of professional vision. *Cogn Technol Work*, 4(2):91–100, 2002.

The paper investigates the work practice of reading mammograms within different screening centres. It highlights how readers interact through the use of external artifacts (i.e. screening reporting form and notation). Although double-reading policy intends to introduce diversity in screening practices, external artifacts support professional interactions and allow knowledge sharing. The results highlight socio-technical artifacts and their role in supporting communities of practice. These results have some implications for the design of technology intended to support work practice. Technology needs to support not only knowledge sharing but also social interactions involved in work practice.

71. Hartswood M, Procter R, Rouncefield M, Slack R. Making a case in medical work: Implications for the electronic medical record. *Comput Supported Coop Work*, 12(3):241–266, 2003.

The paper reports a study of work practices in a toxicology ward within a hospital. It questions the underlying assumptions for the introduction of an

Electronic Medical Record. Although the overall objective is to achieve information integration and sharing across healthcare services, the paper questions whether or not technology innovation can effectively deliver it. The paper highlights that Healthcare practices negotiate and interpret available information. The negotiation and interaction around medical records define and deviate patient trajectories. The paper argues that new technology needs to support not only the integration and sharing of information, but also work practices, professional interactions and memberships that negotiate and interpret local knowledge. The ability to support work practices and interactions happening around information records would also support organisational memory and learning. The paper discusses the implication for the design, implementation and deployment of new technology within complex organisational settings, such as healthcare services.

72. Hartswood M, Procter R, Rouncefield M, Slack R, Soutter J, Voss A. 'Repairing' the Machine: A Case Study of Evaluation of Computer-Aided Detection Tools in Breast Screening. In Dourish P, Fitzpatrick G, editors, *Proceedings of the Eighth European Conference on Computer Supported Cooperative Work*, pages 375–394, 2003.

The paper assesses the impact of computer-based tools in supporting breast screening. Results emphasise various socio-technical aspects of the contingencies between work practice and (dependable) technology. In particular, the ethnographic study points out how technology interaction needs to take into account relevant work practice capturing professional as well as social relationships. The results highlight decision-making processes as distributed cognition relying on different available artifacts. Moreover, they stress the nature of work practice as social collaborative processes among (groups of) professionals (i.e. communities of practice). Emerging *trust*, therefore, acquires an important role in mediating interaction between people and with technology. The paper argues that the design of (new) technology needs to take into account the rich spectrum of social interactions in order to support work practice, hence, communities of practice.

73. Hartswood M, Procter R, Slack R, Soutter J, Voß A, Rouncefield M. The benefits of a long engagement: From contextual design to the co-realisation of work affording artefacts. In *Proceedings of NordiCHI*, pages 283–286. ACM, 2002.

The paper questions the underlying principles of contextual design. Contextual design correctly emphasises the understanding of the application domain, although it still keeps, as the paper argues, a separation between application and design domains. This gap between application and design domains inhibits the benefits of understanding the application domain. Moreover, it exposes the rigidity of contextual design. The paper argues that co-realisation addresses the limitations of contextual design by advocating design in use principles. Understanding the application domain requires technology designers, or facilitators, to foster relationships like membership within the application domain. This enables technology designers and users to explore and to assess different potential solutions in use.

74. Hollnagel E. *Human Reliability Analysis: Context and Control*. Academic Press, 1993.

The book provides a critical introduction to *Human Reliability Analysis*. It stresses how the term 'human error' is misleading and incorrect, because it provides an insufficient and incomplete account of human performance with respect to reliability and technical systems. Subtle interactions between system coupling, complexity and human performance highlight the paradox of how technology innovation exposes human performance to technological hazards giving rise to phenomena like, for instance, *risk homeostasis*. Combining qualitative and quantitative aspects (e.g. of human performance) enhances our understanding of the mechanisms underlying Human Reliability Analysis. The book introduces basic models of Human Reliability Analysis. The models and their underlying assumptions expose the limitations of the separations between human factors and systems. Unveiling the relationship between human performance and reliability requires an understanding of human cognition processes. The book stresses that it is necessary to understand the relationship between human performance and reliability within the specific context, that is, the whole *system*.

75. HSE. Taking account of societal concerns about risk—framing the problem. Research Report 035, Health & Safety Executive, 2002.

The report stresses the importance of analysing risk from a societal viewpoint. It discusses three different types of risk: *directly perceptible, perceived with the help of science* and *virtual risks*. These types of risk are further refined into risks that are voluntary or imposed. It discusses how risk management is about balancing different relevant rewards (of dealing properly with risks) or costs (of failing to deal with them). The report discusses rewards and costs from a societal viewpoint. It uses social lenses (i.e. *individualist, egalitarian, fatalist* and *hierarchist*) drawn from the Cultural Theory of risk in order to explain how risk is individual. Hence, risk management needs to take into account such aspects. In particular, it needs to explain what types of risk it is dealing with and to whom risk might concern. This also suggests not adopting single-metric methods such as cost benefit analysis, but to develop risk analysis discourses that account for different societal perspectives.

76. HSE. A review of safety culture and safety climate literature for the development of the safety culture inspection toolkit. Research Report 367, Health & Safety Executive, 2005.

The report discusses various aspects of safety culture and safety climate. It reviews relevant literature, techniques and tools (e.g. safety culture questionnaires) in order to highlight critical aspects defining safety culture.

It identifies five major safety culture indicators: leadership, two-way communication, employee involvement, learning culture and attitude towards blame. The report stresses that these indicators should inform health and safety management methods and practices.

77. HSL. *Safety Culture: A review of the literature.* HSL/2002/25, Health & Safety Laboratory, 2002.

The report reviews relevant literature on safety culture. It discusses the notions of safety culture and safety climate. Although the term safety culture seems to be "more embracing than that of safety climate", the terms are often used interchangeably. The report stresses how management's attitudes and behaviours influence organisational safety culture.

78. Hughes AC, Hughes TP, editors. *Systems, Experts, and Computers: The Systems Approach in Management and Engineering, World War II and After.* The MIT Press, 2000.

This collection highlights how a systems approach, with its origins in the military domain, pervaded and gave rise to engineering and management. The systems approach provides a holistic vision of engineering and management. It stresses a focus on heterogeneous subsystems or components and their interconnections and interfaces. Systems consist of diverse parts, e.g. technical or managerial, which often mirror each other. The essays in this collection highlight how the systems approach embraces the experience of different communities of practice. It is still possible to find the main principles underlying the systems approach in current engineering and management disciplines. Of particular interest is how the systems approach influenced practice in engineering and managing computer-based systems and their use in safety-critical domains. The intrinsic complexity of engineering safe computer-based systems shaped and triggered debates among practitioners (e.g. engineers) and scholars (e.g. computer scientists). These debates emphasised the human factors 'problem' with respect to safe human-computer interactions in computer-based systems. The complexity required further effort and development in assuring computer-based safety cases. The historical accounts of the development of the systems approach highlight the nature of 'modern' engineering and management of computer-based systems (and expose the limitations).

79. International Electrotechnical Commission. *IEC 61508: Functional safety of electrical/electronic/programmable electronic safety-related systems*, 2.0 edition, 2010.

It is an international standard defining the main principles of functional safety. The IEC 61508 consists of different parts (i.e. Part 1 general requirements, Part 2 requirements for electrical/electronic/programmable electronic safety-related systems, Part 3 software requirements, Part 4 definitions and abbreviations, Part 5 examples of methods for the determination of safety integrity levels,

Part 6 guidelines on the application of IEC 61508-2 and IEC 61508-3, and Part 7 overview of techniques and measures). Part 3 on software requirements, in particular, applies to any software forming part of a safety-critical system or used to develop a safety-critical system. The standard is intended to address the needs of different safety-critical industries (e.g. automotive, railways, nuclear) that rely on computer-based systems. It also provides an account of risk. It stresses that risk is always present and has to be reduced ALARP (As Low As Reasonably Practicable).

80. Jeffcott MA, Johnson CW. The Use of a Formalised Risk Model in NHS Information System Development. *Cogn Technol Work*, 4(2):120–136, 2002.

The paper points out the necessity to using risk analysis in the design and deployment of *Information Systems* and, in general, technology in complex organisational settings like the British National Health Service (NHS). Such complex systems expose the limitations of methodologies, e.g. Hazards and Operability Analysis (HAZOP), Failure Modes, Effect and Criticality Analysis (FMECA) and Human Reliability Analysis (HRA), relying on Probabilistic Risk Assessment (PRA). In particular, it argues that such methodologies provide a limited account of organisational issues. This is due to a lack of modelling of organisational features in terms of *environment*, as "the aggregate of social and cultural conditions that influence the life of an individual or community", and *context*, as "encompassing all the factors outside the control of risk assessment", i.e. "the structure and culture of the organization that cannot, if at all, be easily changed". The paper applies an enriched risk assessment model, capturing *History*, *Internal context*, *External context*, *Content*, *Processes* and *Risk outcomes*, to the investigation of two cases studies. The results emphasise the benefits of analysing and understanding organisational issues, which complement PRA.

81. Johnson C. The causes of human error in medicine. *Cogn Technol Work*, 4(2):65–70, 2002.

The paper provides a *systemic* analysis of *'human error'* in medicine. It describes different (hierarchical) levels (i.e. individual behaviour, team-based performance, management of health care applications, and involvement of regulatory and governmental organisations) of causal factors. It discusses the different drivers for an increasing concern over medical failures or poor medical practices. In particular, it points to the economic pressure over medical services and the increase of public risk perception. Although the increasing concern over medical failures has favoured public awareness, it paradoxically inhibits and undermines technology innovation in medical domains. The paper also presents recent research results providing further evidence of how a systemic view of causal factors enriches our understanding of 'human errors' in medicine.

82. Johnson CW. *Failure in Safety-Critical Systems: A Handbook of Accident and Incident Reporting*. University of Glasgow Press, 2003.

The book gives a comprehensive description of techniques for incident reporting systems. The analysis of the main sources of failure stresses and motivates the implementation and maintenance of incident reporting systems. Unfortunately, many organisations yet face practical as well as technical problems in implementing incident reporting systems. This book provides a guidance for establishing (large-scale) incident reporting systems. The book draws guidelines and reviews relevant theories and methodologies from various industry and service domains. Finally, it highlights barriers that organisations need to address in order to successfully implement incident reporting systems across many industries.

83. Johnson CW. What are emergent properties and how do they affect the engineering of complex systems? *Reliab Eng Syst Saf*, 91(12):1475–1481, 2006.

The paper is the editorial introduction to a special issue on "Complexity in Design and Engineering". It provides an initial introduction to various accounts of "emergence" and "complexity". It stresses how emergence and complexity are multi-facet aspects of systems. It points out a lack of agreement and a limited understanding of emergent properties with respect to the design and engineering of complex systems. It highlights the controversial aspects that emergent properties have for technology risk (assessment). It draws some implications of emergence for engineering complex systems.

84. Kaptelinin V, Nardi BA. *Acting with Technology: Activity Theory and Interaction Design*. MIT Press, 2006.

The book provides an historical account of the developments of *Activity Theory* in the context of *interaction design*. It reviews the theoretical foundations of activity theory and, by comparative analysis, positions activity theory with respect to other approaches of theories, among which Human-Computer Interaction (HCI), Computer-Supported Collaborative Work (CSCW), Distributed Cognition and Actor-Network Theory (ANT). It analyses the contribution of activity theory with respect to interaction design.

85. Klein HK, Kleinman DL. The social construction of technology: Structural considerations. *Sci Technol Hum Values*, 27(1):28–52, 2002.

The paper is concerned with the theory of the *Social Construction Of Technology* (SCOT) and reexamines the main framework's components: *interpretive flexibility, relevant social groups, closure* (and *stabilisation*) and (sociocultural and political) *context*. The paper discusses their main limitations with respect to structural considerations of technology. In particular, it argues that the SCOT framework, although it highlights the importance, in particular, of social groups in the design of technology, provides limited account of structural aspects of them and their relevance. The paper extends the SCOT framework by highlighting the importance of structural considerations with respect to relevant groups. It discusses how structural considerations enhance our understanding of the mechanisms involved in the design of technology or in processes of technical change. In conclusions, the paper stresses the importance of structural considerations of relevant social groups with respect to technology design and change.

86. Küster Filipe J, Felici M, Anderson S. Timed knowledge-based modelling and analysis: On the dependability of socio-technical systems. In *Proceedings of HAAMAHA 2003, 8th International Conference on Human Aspects of Advanced Manufacturing: Agility & Hybrid Automation*, pages 321–328, 2003.

This paper is concerned with the analysis of socio-technical systems, in particular, safety-critical systems involving considerable human intervention. Experience shows that evolving knowledge distribution in socio-technical systems may trigger catastrophic events affecting system dependability. This paper presents a knowledge-based approach to model and analyse evolving scenarios in socio-technical systems. The timed knowledge-based approach captures the nature of socio-technical systems, which consist of hybrid resources continuously interacting with each other. The analysis and modelling of a case study drawn from the Air Traffic Control domain shows the applicability of the proposed approach.

87. Latour B. Is Re-modernization Occurring—And If So, How to Prove It? A Commentary on Ulrich Beck. *Theory Cult Soc*, 20(2):35–48, 2003.

The paper questions the theory of *re-modernisation*, that is, the existence of diverse modernities. The analysis of re-modernisation draws a comparison between the *actor-network theory* (ANT) and the *risk society*. The paper rejects the term "modern" as often advocated by technologists. It argues that, on the contrary, we "have never been modern". The paper analyses features (e.g. reflexive behaviours, externalities) of "modern" societies with respect to the similarities and differences between actor-network and risk theories. It argues that although re-modernisation might or not be happening, evidence is still patchy. Finally, The paper points out similarities and differences between the actor-network theory and the risk society.

88. Le Coze J. Are organisations too complex to be integrated in the technical risk assessment and current safety auditing? *Saf Sci*, 43(8):613–638, 2005.

The paper discusses various organisational issues affecting safety. In particular, it highlights the relationship between organisation and complexity. It argues that an analysis of relevant complexity and organisational aspects should be part of auditing processes. The paper stresses "the difficulty of introducing the complex nature of organisations into integrated methodologies [...], and discusses the perspective of introducing it into current safety auditing practices."

89. Le Coze J. Disasters and organisations: From lessons learnt to theorising. *Saf Sci*, 46(1):132–149, 2008.

The paper discusses various organisational aspects that are relevant for accident investigations. In particular, it identifies a multi-dimensional framework for classifying investigative models. The framework identifies different organisational levels (i.e. "micro/meso/macro") and different investigative approaches (i.e. "normative" or prescriptive as opposed to *"descriptive"* modelling and models). The combination of these dimensions enables different types of investigations. It allows an analysis of different causalities with respect to organisational dimensions and types of investigations.

90. Leveson NG. *SAFEWARE: System Safety and Computers.* Addison-Wesley, 1995.

The book analyses the risk of software in complex systems. It highlights contingencies between reliability and safety. The analysis of the nature of risk and the causes of accidents stresses differences between software and hardware. It emphasises safety as a emergent system property, rather than a property of the individual parts forming complex systems. The book also describes the basic elements of "design for safety". Moreover, It provides an analysis of several accidents that occurred within various systems. In particular, it provides an analysis of the accidents that occurred with the medical device Therac-25. The study highlights contingencies between software reliability, system safety and organisational culture to safety.

91. Licoppe C, Smoreda Z. Are social networks technologically embedded? How networks are changing today with changes in communication technology. *Soc Networks*, 27(4):317–335, 2005.

The paper analyzes how nowadays social networks use available technology, in particular, *Information and Communication Technologies* (ICT), in order to maintain their social ties. It highlights how technology mediated relationships rely on available technology. On the other hand, technology enables sociability and re-draws social boundaries with respect to distance (i.e. relationship remotely located at various distance) and timeliness (i.e. timing distribution of social interactions). This emphasises the tightly coupling between social networks and technology.

92. Littlewood B, Popov P, Strigini L. Modeling software design diversity: A review. *ACM Comput Surv*, 33(2):177–208, 2001.

The paper reviews modelling software design diversity. It provides a comprehensive introduction and review of modelling methodologies for software design diversity. It highlights theoretical as well as practical difficulties in modelling diverse systems. Moreover, it points out contingencies between reliability and diversity. The paper describes research results and identifies open issues with respect ‚to modelling software design diversity.

93. Littlewood B, Wright D. The use of multi-legged arguments to increase confidence in safety claims for software-based systems: A study based on a

BBN analysis of an idealised example. *IEEE Trans on Softw Eng*, 33(5): 347–365, 2007.

The paper develops a probabilistic account —based on a Bayesian Belief Network (BBN)—of the *confidence* (that is, "the probability that a claim is true") over the combination of multi-legged arguments (e.g. supporting safety claims). The analytical development of the confidence of multi-legged arguments unveils contingencies in the general assumption that "two supporting arguments are better than one". The idealised example points out counter-intuitive situations in which evidence supporting one argument, could "accidentally" decrease our overall confidence. This highlights subtle contingencies between the dependency between the assumptions underlying the individual arguments forming the multi-legged one. Therefore, although it is possible two derive individual arguments from a multi-legged one, there are contingencies in the combination of individual arguments into a structured multi-legged one. The paper advocates for further analytical developments in order to understand contingencies affecting our confidence in multi-legged arguments.

94. Löfstedt RE, Frewer L, editors. *The Earthscan Reader in Risk and Modern Society*. Earthscan Publications, 1998.

A collection of relevant work that provides an account of the diverse aspects of risk. The different contributions identify and discuss major research areas (e.g. psychometric paradigm, social construction of risk, cultural theory, amplification of risk, trust) that concern risk.

95. Lutters WG, Ackerman MS. Achieving safety: A field study of boundary objects in aircraft technical support. In *Proceedings of the 2002 ACM conference on Computer Supported Cooperative Work, CSCW '02*, pages 266–275. ACM Press, 2002.

The paper reports a case study drawn from the aircraft domain. The case study investigates in terms of boundary objects the coordination and information flow between different organisational groups. The empirical results emphasise how achieving safety is an organisational process that relies on shared boundary objects. Boundary objects provide a means of coordinating and information sharing between different organisational groups, who might have competing or diverging interests. Understanding the mechanisms and processes underpinning boundary objects enhances our understanding of achieving safety in complex organisational settings.

96. MacKenzie D. *Mechanizing Proof: Computing, Risk, and Trust*. The MIT Press, 2001.

Computer systems pervade diverse communities of practices. The book investigates the nature of knowledge. A socio-historical account analyses the nature of knowledge taking into account its diverse origins, i.e. induction, authority and deduction. The book investigates how trust in computer systems and their contribution to the creation of knowledge has influenced developments of modern mathematics. Moreover, it highlights the developments of computer systems and their usage in order to support recent developments of mathematics and proofs. It provides a sociological account of the relationship between risk, trust and knowledge.

97. MacKenzie D. Physics and Finance: S-Terms and Modern Finance as a Topic for Science Studies. *Sci Technol Hum Values*, 26(2):115–144, 2001.

The paper discusses the nature of modern finance and justifies an interest for social studies. It highlights three main aspects of modern finance: first, the changing disciplinary boundary of economics; second, the distinction between private and public knowledge; third, the legal and cultural demarcation between legitimate trading and gambling. Finally, the paper emphasises, by means of the historical study of Long-Term Capital Management (LTCM), that modern finance presents indeed instances of S-terms (social kind), as opposed to N-terms (natural kind), and S-loops, or feedback loops, (i.e. self-referential and self-validating). However, the LTCM experience points out that there are contingencies between S-loops and the nature of performativity of modern finance, that is, S-loops may give rise to negative feedback.

98. MacKenzie D. An Equation and its Worlds: Bricolage, Exemplars, Disunity and Performativity in Financial Economics. *Soc Stud Sci*, 33(6):831–868, 2003.

The paper analyses the history of the *option pricing equation*. Despite its mathematical formulation the analysis highlights how the historical formation presents an evolution due to economic practices rather than purely mathematical reasoning. The paper points out and discusses the main emerging characteristics: *bricolage*, *exemplars*, *disunity* and *performativity*. The option pricing equation is a work of bricolage due to many scholars being involved in tackling practical problems of understanding and mimicking financial economics. Its evolution is partially due to the way people adopted mathematical formulae and relevant underlying assumptions in order to apply its formulation into practice. The diversity of the studies tackling the problem became its robustness. Finally, the option pricing equation became performative in the sense that it modified the world it was describing. The more people were adopting the option pricing equation, the better the underlying assumptions became realistic.

99. MacKenzie D. Long-Term Capital Management and the sociology of arbitrage. *Econ Soc*, 32(3):349–380, 2003.

The paper analyses the crisis of Long-Term Capital Management (LTCM). *Arbitrage* is a key process that supports the hypothesis of an efficient market. It allows markets to be positioned as efficient without all investors being assumed to be rational. Although arbitrage is fundamental in the practice of financial markets, it partially explains LTCM's crisis. The paper provides a socio-historical account of the crisis and highlights three main aspects that expose the limitations of the arbitrage thesis to the crisis. First, trading involved people who often established personal relationship (e.g. trust, resentment, jealousy). Second, People involved in trading interact each other. A possible type of interaction is by imitation. Third, imitation gave rise to a *global microstructure* with reduced diversity in arbitrage strategies among people involved in trading. The paper highlights and discusses that these social factors, grounded in the Actor-Network Theory (ANT), emerging in the LTCM crisis expose the limitations of arbitrage to separate the economic from the social, i.e. the technical from the social. This points out the limits of the permormativity of economics.

100. MacKenzie D. The big, bad wolf and the rational market: portfolio insurance, the 1987 crash and the performativity of economics. *Econ Soc*, 33(3):303–334, 2004.

The paper analyses the 1987 stock market crash and its dependence relationship with the performances and mechanisms of *portfolio insurance*. The historical analysis takes into account two different meanings of performativity: *general performativity* and *Austinian performativity*. The paper analyses the forms of performativities emerging in the historical account of economics. Although the stock market crash exhibited some pervormativities, it argues that the underlying theory (or set of adopted models) provided an instance of *conuterperformativity*: "its widespread adoption can undermine the preconditions of its own empirical validity".

101. MacKenzie D. Social connectivities in global financial markets. *Environ Plan D: Soc Space*, 22(1):83–101, 2004.

The paper analyses social aspects of the global financial market. It considers thee basic notions of social connectivity, grounded in the sociological aspects of actor-network theory: mutual susceptibility, imitation and hard factors in societies. The analysis of different forms of trading (i.e. face-to-face, technology-mediated and anonymous) highlights how social connectivities influence global financial markets. The paper argues that it is possible to identify social connectivities in all markets.

102. MacKenzie D. *An Engine, Not a Camera: How Financial Models Shape Markets*. Inside Technology. The MIT Press, 2006.

The book is a socio-historical account of the theories underpinning modern economics. It investigates the *performativity* of financial models and their limitations as *counterperformativity*. Therefore, it provides a socio-historical account of the theories that created, while describing, modern economics. Financial economics, in this sense, is "an engine, not a camera", that is, "an active force transforming its environment, not a camera passively recording it". The book also analyses some of the mechanisms (e.g. *imitation*) that characterise and let modern global markets emerge. This allows us a parallelism between cascades of technology developments, or determinism of technology innovation, and cascades in social science. It unveils the limitations of the cascades in explaining and capturing the complexity of modern financial markets as well as technology innovation.

103. MacKenzie D, Wajcman J, editors. *The Social Shaping of Technology*. Open University Press, second edition, 1999.

The collection pinpoints theories underlying the social shaping of technology. The revision and discussion of different theories and case studies highlight the relationship between the social and technical aspects of technology. This allows the critical revision of various theories and perspectives undermining the social contributions towards technology innovation. The collection of papers highlights how technology innovation unveiling as technology trajectories unfold under the stimulus of peculiar socio-technical conditions.

104. MacKenzie D, Millo Y. Constructing a Market, Performing Theory: The Historical Sociology of a Financial Derivatives Exchange. *Am J Sociol*, 109(1):107–145, 2003.

The paper provides a socio-historical account of the Chicago Board Options Exchange (CBOE). Although *performativity* captures to some extent the underlying processes of the establishment of the CBOE and theoretical foundations, mainly the option pricing model, the performativity of economics has some limits. In particular, the notion of *embedding* grounded in action-network theory stresses the role of *culture* and *moral communities* in which *collective actions* arose. Moreover, this emphasises two other aspects. First is that human beings have *bounded rationality* as opposed to the rational actor account. Second, economic action is *distributed cognition*. These further stress the limits of the performativity of economics.

105. MacKenzie DA. *Inventing Accuracy: A Historical Sociology of Nuclear Missile Guidance*. The MIT Press, 1990.

Technology often seems to have an evolutionary momentum driven by technological arguments. Changes in technology form a "natural" *trajectory of technology*. However, the historical and sociological analysis of the evolution of missile accuracy points out new insights to analysing the evolution of technology. Technology innovation results from technical changes situated in particular social and political situations. Technical changes overcome knowledge uncertainties under the pressure of social and political perceptions. Either technical, social and political aspects interact in the production process of engineering technology innovation. This highlights the heterogeneous nature of engineering processes, hence *heterogeneous engineering*. Therefore, the *institutionalisation* of a pattern of technological change requires the existence of a relatively stable organisational framework together with the availability and commitment of resources (e.g. knowledge) in order for technology innovation to take place. This stresses how diverse socio-technical aspects influence technology changes.

106. MacKenzie DA. *Knowing Machines: Essays on Technical Change*. The MIT Press, 1996.

The book is a collection of different contributions. The main body of knowledge addresses the analysis and investigation of technological changes. Social theories provide alternative perspectives to technical and economical analysis of technological evolution. Although post analysis of technology development highlights *technology trajectories*, social theories argue against the existence on a *normal trajectory of technology* purely driven by technological arguments. Reasons for technology changes find ground in *heterogeneous engineering*, the engineering of the physical as well as of the social world, which highlights the *social shaping of technology*.

107. Martin D, Hartswood M, Slack R, Voss A. Achieving Dependability in the Configuration, Integration and Testing of Healthcare Technologies. *Comput Supported Coop Work*, 15(5–6):467–499, 2006.

The paper reports two case studies drawn from the healthcare domain. The case studies use ethnographic (observational) methods and provide examples of various dependability concerns arising. These examples draw an understanding of dependability with respect to work practices and organisational boundaries. They depict dependability as "contexted", that is, as resulting from various socio-technical aspects put in context.

108. Monk A, Hone K, Lines L, Dowdall A, Baxter G, Blythe M, Wright P. Towards a practical framework for managing the risks of selecting technology to support independent living. *Appl Ergonomics*, 37(5):599–606, 2006.

The paper is concerned with technology applications that may increase the independence and quality of life of older people or people with disabilities. It proposes a risk management framework to assist in selecting applications that match the requirements of individuals. The framework supports a risk analysis, picking up concepts from risk analysis in other domains, tailored for the particular social application domain. The risk management framework identifies Activities of Daily Living (ADLs) and events to drive the risk analysis. It also identifies Generic Types of Harm (GTH) and their likely consequences. The risk analysis then assess the likelihood and the severity of the potential harms due to some incident in conducting the daily activities. This allows the identification of scenarios describing potential hazards or mishaps. The risk analysis involves four steps: (1) defining the objectives of the risk analysis and its scope, (2) risk analysis of the current situation, (3) risk analysis of the planned system, and (4) post-installation risk analysis. The paper, finally, shows a sample application of the risk management framework.

The example uses a rich picture describing a scenario and stressing the social relationships involving various individuals, organisations or services.

109. Mythen G. *Ulrich Beck: A Critical Introduction to the Risk Society*. Pluto Press, 2004.

The book reviews the "risk society" thesis. It questions the underlying principles in order to investigate and address various aspects of risk. The discussion of various aspects of risk exposes some limitations of the "risk society" thesis with respect to the subtle complex nature of risk.

110. Nardi BA, Whittaker S, Schwarz H. NetWORKers and their Activity in Intensional Networks. *Comput Supported Coop Work*, 11(1–2):205–242, 2002.

The emergence of *personal social networks*—a "netWORK"—called *Intensional Networks*, characterises cooperative work. The paper introduces the notion of intensional networks as form of collaboration—social networks—across organisational boundaries. The *building, maintaining* and *activating* of social networks are critical activities of cooperation. The paper compares intensional networks to other forms of networking, such as *communities of practice, knots, coalitions, actor-networks* and networks of *strong and weak ties*. Although they exhibit different characteristics, all of them stress the importance of understanding emerging social networks and their interactions. Moreover, understanding social networks becomes more and more important for the design and deployment of technology.

111. Neumann PG. *Computer Related Risks*. The ACM Press, 1995.

The book provides a review of computer related risks. It takes mainly into account a system viewpoint in order to understand and analyse computer risk. The main sources of risks considered are engineering issues arising in system development, operation and use. The book then provides a review of known accidents in specific application domain (e.g. communication systems, civil aviation, medical health and safety). The accident review highlights key issues affecting system reliability, safety, security and integrity. The review exposes the limitations in analysing, characterising and addressing computer related risks from a narrow engineering viewpoint. It then extends the analysis to systemic and human factors viewpoints identifying diverse, rather than engineering, sources of *computer related risks*.

112. Norman DA. *Things that make us smart: defining human attributes in the age of the machine*. Perseus Books, 1993.

The book discusses the nature of human cognition. In particular, it describes the theory of *Distributed Cognition*. It investigates the interaction between representational resources, which can be located within the human mind as well as external artifacts. It helps to understand how information mediated activities are carried out by distributed resources. It stresses how human cognition extends the boundaries of human minds, that is, it extends to external distributed artifacts. Distributed cognition highlights how internal and external artifacts interact in human cognition.

113. Perrow C. *Normal Accidents: Living with High-Risk Technologies*. Princeton University Press, 1999.

The book defines a risk framework for analysing and classifying technological systems. The framework identifies two major dimensions: *complexity* and *coupling*. The former classifies systems according to the complexity and interactions of failures, e.g. linear or complex interactions. The latter classifies systems according to the coupling between system parts. This framework classifies systems according to their combined complexity and coupling. The more complex and tight the coupling, the higher the risks. The framework then drives the analysis of different industry domains (e.g. petrochemical plants, aircraft and airways). It supports a risk analysis, according to complexity and coupling, forming the basics of, namely, *Normal Accident Theory* (NAT). The book, finally, highlights different rationalities (i.e. *absolute*, *bounded* and *social*) in risk assessment processes.

114. Petroski H. *To Engineer is Human: The Role of Failure in Successful Design*. Vintage Books, 1982.

The analysis of (civil) engineering failures allows the characterisation of design engineering as human activity. Design failures are a means to acquire experience in engineering (i.e. learning by failures). As (design) innovation involves risk, engineering involves the foresight and mitigation of *known* hazards into future design. Engineering knowledge is acquired by subsequent design refinements and decisions. The design process, therefore, involves an evolutionary cycle of design *improvements* or *corrections*, which take into account system failures. Therefore, engineering design captures innovations as well as lessons learned from system failures. The attempt to classify system failures, as well as to identify the causes of failures, highlights some issues with classifications of failures. The problems with classifications may involve a lack of accountability and responsibility in engineering design and tools.

115. Petroski H. *Design Paradigms: Case Histories of Error and Judgment in Engineering*. Cambridge University Press, 1994.

Design errors have a crucial role in *engineering thinking* and *judgement*. The analysis of engineering failures, drawn from bridge constructions, allows the characterisation of engineering thinking and judgement. Case histories of error and judgement in engineering highlight design paradigms, which pinpoint the contribution of error analysis in innovative design. Proactive failure analysis enables *learning from failures*. This process of analysing case histories of failures is at the foundation of Petroski's design paradigms. On the other hand, design failures emerge as failures to learn from previous experience. Social and political aspects affect at certain time risk perception allowing design errors to emerge or happen again. The histories of failures and the trust on engineering tools (e.g. analytical or computational models) therefore enable the learning process that results in engineering thinking and judgement.

116. Pidgeon N, O'Leary M. Man-made disasters: why technology and organizations (sometimes) fail. *Saf Sci*, 34(1–3):15–30, 2000.

The paper discusses the nature of organisational failures with technology. An analysis of large-scale accidents identifies the problems arising in the technology and organisation interaction as the main causes of failures. The paper identifies and discusses two common barriers—i.e. information difficulties, and blame and organisational politics—to organisational learning.

117. Popov P. Reliability Assessment of Legacy Safety-Critical Systems Upgraded with Off-the-Shelf Components. In Anderson S, Bologna S, Felici M, editors, *Proceedings of the 21st International Conference on Computer Safety, Reliability and Security, SAFECOMP 2002*, number 2434 in LNCS, pages 139–150. Springer-Verlag, 2002.

The reliability assessment becomes problematic under maintenance activities. System upgrades with Commercial-Off-The-Shelf (COTS) components make it difficult to rely on previous system knowledge. Knowledge uncertainty and structural complexity expose the limitations of modelling and predicting system reliability by Bayesian approaches. On the one hand, new components (e.g. COTS) enable conservative assumptions on system reliability. On the other hand, structural complexity explodes and translates exponentially into Bayesian models. Unrealistic assumptions, such as independence of failures, can be misleading about actual system reliability. Moreover, it is often unfeasible to support them, because such assumptions demand substantial efforts (e.g. in terms of long acceptance testing) for their validity. This seriously limits the applicability of Bayesian approaches in order to estimate system reliability subject to system upgrades, generally, system changes.

118. Popov P, Littlewood B. The effect of testing on reliability of fault-tolerant software. In *Proceedings of the 2004 International Conference on Dependable Systems and networks, DSN'04*, pages 265–274. IEEE Computer Society, 2004.

The paper takes account of the evolution of individual versions in probabilistic modelling of (forced) diversity. The modelling extends early stochastic accounts of diversity. In particular, it takes into account the effect of testing on diversity in which individual versions evolve due to the selection of (statistically independent) test suites and fault fixing, hence, on the reliability of fault-tolerant software. It highlights the conditions for which the assumptions of independence hold. Although the application and evaluation of some aspects of modelling are still challenging in practice, the modelling provides a stochastic account of the evolution of diverse software.

119. Procter R, Rouncefield M, Balka E, Berg M. Special Issue: CSCW and Dependable Healthcare Systems. *Comput Supported Coop Work*, 15(5–6): 413–418, December 2006.

The paper is the introduction to a special issue that stresses how the Interdisciplinary Research Collaboration on Dependability enhances our understanding of complex organisational settings. In particular, the special issue is concerned with various dependable healthcare systems. It also advocates dependability as an emergent property of Computer Supported Cooperative Work (CSCW).

120. Reason J. *Managing the Risks of Organizational Accidents*. Ashgate, 1997.

The book analyses *failures* as "organisational accidents". Failures, or losses, emerge due to hazards exposing the limitations of hierarchical organisational barriers. The analysis of the different contributing factors provides a characterisation of the *"Swiss cheese" model* of organisational defences. This model allows the identification of hierarchical stages in the development and investigation of an organisational accident, from unsafe acts through local workplace factors to organisational factors. Moreover, it emphasises safety culture from an organisational viewpoint.

121. Robertson B, Sribar V. *The Adaptive Enterprise: IT Infrastructure Strategies to Manage Change and Enable Growth*. IT Best Practice Series. Addison-Wesley, 2002.

The book provides a practitioner viewpoint of managing and evolving Information Technology (IT) infrastructures. In particular, it discusses patterns and processes for the development of IT infrastructures supporting organisational change—driven by business needs.

122. Rogers Y, Scaife M, Rizzo A. Interdisciplinarity: an emergent or engineered process? In Derry SJ, Schunn CD, Gernsbacher MA, editors, *Interdisciplinary Collaboration: An Emerging Cognitive Science*. Lawrence Erlbaum Associates, 2005.

The paper questions the nature of *interdisciplinarity* as well as *multidisciplinarity*. The paper argues that interdisciplinary work culd be an ideal target in practice. It draws on the analysis of recent developments in cognitive science of disciplines such as Human-Computer Interaction (HCI) and Computer Supported Cooperative Work (CSCW). Although multidisciplinary work often faces difficulties in practice (e.g. lack of common understanding or language among diverse disciplines), the paper stresses how multidisciplinary work could be a strategy for overcoming limitations "within" single disciplines. The adaptation of artifacts (e.g. models, concepts) drawn from other disciplines into an integrated framework support the seeking of understanding of complex problems, which remain unresolved or incomprehensible within single disciplines. These mechanisms allow us to tackle complex, otherwise unresolved or incomprehensible, problems into emerging "interdisciplinary" accounts, which characterise "solutions" into an integrated framework arising from diverse disciplines and filling knowledge gaps within and between disciplines.

123. Rushby J. Using model checking to help discover mode confusions and other automation surprises. *Reliab Eng Syst Saf*, 75(2):167–177, 2002.

The paper uses model checking to unveil inconsistencies between system behaviour and mental models (both represented as state transition systems). It discusses the formal analysis of cognitive aspects of technology interaction resulting in mode confusions or other automation surprises.

124. Slovic P. *The Perception of Risk*. Earthscan Publications, 2000.

The book presents the "psychometric paradigm" of risk perception. It reviews the developments of the psychometric paradigm, its development and research results in risk perception. Empirical results rely on the use of questionnaires in order to sample people's perception on diverse (e.g. technological and environmental) hazards and to quantitatively as well as qualitatively assess risk. The psychometric paradigm highlights several factors influencing risk perception. For instance, it points out how various socio-cultural aspects affect risk perception. Moreover, there is an effect of the social amplification of risk. The psychometric paradigm provides insights on the early development on risk perceptions. Empirical results point to research directions that were further developed from diverse perspectives (e.g. socio and cultural aspects of risk perception).

125. Smith SP, Harrison MD. Reuse in hazard analysis: Identification and support. In Anderson S, Felici M, Littlewood B, editors, *Proceedings of the 22nd International Conference on Computer Safety, Reliability and Security, SAFECOMP 2003*, number 2788 in LNCS, pages 382–395. Springer-Verlag, 2003.

The paper investigates the reuse of hazard analysis in two case studies. The first case study is concerned with reuse in the construction of safety arguments. The analysis identifies structured arguments in the hazard analysis. Therefore, it is possible to assess the amount of reuse. A substantial reuse could be misleading and give the impression of rigorous coverage. This is obviously undesirable for the dependability analysis of safety-critical systems. However, the amount of reuse provides limited indication about the validity of safety cases. In order to support the construction of safety arguments, the analysis needs to determine whether or not there exist suitable reusable arguments. The second study is concerned with reuse changes resulting from tool support. Although tool support enables the tailoring of reused arguments. Most reused arguments are adapted trivially. A proposed edit distance algorithm allows the identification and the enumeration of reused safety arguments.

126. Smith SP, Harrison MD. Measuring reuse in hazard analysis. *Reliab Eng Syst Saf*, 89(1):93–104, 2005.

Hazard and safety analyses for safety-critical systems are major activities in order to assess whether the risk associated with any specific design is acceptable. However, they require sufficient coverage and rigour to provide enough evidence that the proposed solutions mitigate the identified risk. This often implies exhaustive hazard and safety analyses, although these are time consuming and error-prone. Reuse is a strategy to reduce the cost of developing hazard and safety analyses. Unfortunately, reuse strategies may affect the effectiveness, correctness and validity of hazard and safety analyses. This paper proposes a method for identifying the amount of reuse in hazard analysis. The proposed method relies on an edit distance algorithm that highlights argument clusters. The paper investigates hazard analysis reuse in two case studies. Both case studies uncover a considerable amount of reuse.

127. Sommerville I. *Software Engineering*. Addison-Wesley, eighth edition, 2007.

It is a textbook on Software Engineering. It introduces the main methodologies addressing different phases (e.g. Requirements, Design, Development, Verification and Validation) of engineering software systems.

128. Stonebumer G, Goguen A, Feringa A. *Risk Management Guide for Information Technology Systems—Recommendations of the National Institute of Standards and Technology*. NIST, July 2002.

These guidelines describe risk management for security of Information Technology (IT) systems. Risk management guidelines rely on a risk assessment process consisting of nine fundamental steps. A critical step is the identification of major threat sources. Human threats identify common groups (e.g. Hackers, Computer criminals, Terrorists). Different groups have different motivations, hence it necessary to identify different threat actions. Another critical step is the identification of the (system) vulnerabilities in terms of vulnerability/threat pairs, for example, with respect to human threats. The risk mitigation involves the implementation of identified options that intend to reduce the identified risk to an acceptable level. Cost-benefit analyses drive the implementation of risk mitigation options. The guidelines describe and identify a general risk management process.

129. Storey N. *Safety-Critical Computer Systems*. Addison-Wesley, 1996.

The book describes various methodologies in designing and assessing safety-critical computer systems. It takes into account various design activities (e.g. from verification, validation, testing to quality management and certification) as well as methodologies (e.g. formal methods) and analyses (e.g. hazard and risk analysis).

130. Strigini L, Povyakalo A, Alberdi E. Human-machine diversity in the use of computer advisory systems: a case study. In *Proceedings of the 2003*

International Conference on Dependable Systems and Networks, DSN'03, pages 249–258. IEEE Computer Society, 2003.

The paper provides a probabilistic modelling of reliability assessment for a class of human-machine systems. In particular, the paper considers advisory systems drawn from the mammography domain, in which a computer system supports screening of mammograms (i.e. X-ray films). The underlying architecture consists of a clear-box model, which distinguishes two main system components, the human and the system component. The probabilistic modelling then assesses how a computer advisory's false negatives affect the performance, in terms of human reliability of detecting false negatives, of the human-machine system. The paper provides useful insights for the modelling, design and improvement of advisory systems. Moreover, it highlights contingencies in the operational profiles due to *indirect* effects (e.g. trust in the advisory system) on the overall system performance.

131. Strum S, Latour B. The meanings of social: From baboons to humans. *Inf Sci Soc*, 26:783–802, 1987.

The paper articulates a theoretical framework for the performativity of social links. The framework highlights the evolution of societies, from *soft* to *hard* societies. The availability of resources allow a shift from *social complexity* to *social complication*. This shift characterises (technology-enabled) modern societies from other primitive societies. Modern societies have learned how to concentrate, allocate and use resources in order to organise others on a large scale. This highlights symmetry between individuals—we are all equal and engage in society to some extent—and asymmetry between individuals in terms of the availability and ability to resource social organisations.

132. Vincenti WG. *What Engineers Know and How They Know It: Analytical Studies from Aeronautical History*. The Johns Hopkins University Press, 1990.

Vincenti's book provides a critical analysis of the nature of *Engineering Knowledge*. The analysis of different case studies drawn from the aviation industry allows the characterisation of engineering as knowledge. This raises *Engineering Science* as related to but distinct from *Science*, not merely a subclass of *Applied Science*. The historical account provides an epistemic analysis of engineering knowledge and its relation to system design, hence the underlying assumption of *Technology as knowledge*. The generalisation of the historical account allows the identification of the underlying characteristics (e.g. categories of knowledge) and mechanisms (knowledge-generating activities) of engineering knowledge. These provide the basis for a variation-selection model for the growth of engineering knowledge. The study furthermore emphasises the important role of communities (e.g. engineers, practitioners) in the creation and mediation of knowledge.

133. Voß A, Procter R, Slack R, Hartswood M, Williams R, Rouncefield M. Accomplishing 'just-in-time' production. In Johnson C, editor, *Human*

Decision Making and Control, GIST Technical Report G2002-1, pages 209–
211, 2002.

The paper discusses a case study drawn from a manufacturing domain. The
case study highlights how local knowledge is embedded into work practice.
This knowledge is complementary to embedded knowledge into technological
artifacts or systems. The unique combination of local knowledge, work
practice and technology enables work arounds addressing dependability
contingencies (or unforeseen events) between work practice and technology.

134. Voß A, Slack R, Procter R, Williams R, Hartswood M, Rouncefield M.
Dependability as ordinary action. In Anderson S, Bologna S, Felici M,
editors, *Proceedings of the 21st International Conference on Computer
Safety, Reliability and Security, SAFECOMP 2002*, number 2434 in LNCS,
pages 32–43. Springer-Verlag, 2002.

Ethnographic studies contribute towards the understanding of the nature of
dependability. Hence, it is possible to analyse dependability as an account of
work practices in socio-technical contexts. The analysis of work practice in
situated contexts highlights how dependable work practice can cope with
system undependability. Work arounds emerge from available organisational
knowledge. Ethnographic studies point out how work practice uses and
selects organisational knowledge in order to identify dependable work
arounds. This stresses contingencies between system dependability and
organisational knowledge as work practice.

135. Wallace DR, Kuhn DR. Lessons from 342 medical device failures.
In *Proceedings of the 4th IEEE International Symposium on High-Assurance
Systems Engineering, HASE*, pages 123–131. IEEE Computer Society, 1999.

The paper analyses software-related failures of medical devices. The study
considers reported failures triggering recalls of various medical devices.
Among the reported failures, 342 of them were due somehow to software
faults. The analysis initially classifies the failure according to the
classification (of the primary function) of the affected functionalities in the
medical devices. Then, the analysis refines the classification and identifies
thirteen primary "symptoms" (e.g. behaviour, data, function, general,
service, system, timing). Hence, the analysis further identifies thirteen
different fault categories. For each of the fault class, the analysis identifies
engineering methodologies or practices, which could had prevented or
selected the specific type of fault. Finally, the paper draws the lessons
learned, in terms of software engineering practice, from the analysis of the
342 failures and relative faults.

136. Wears RL, Cook RI, Perry SJ. Automation, interaction, complexity, and
failure: A case study. *Reliab Eng Syst Saf*, 91(12):1494–1501, 2006.

The paper discusses a case study drawn from the healthcare domain.
It emphasises how the introduction of new technology exposes organisations

to new vulnerabilities due to subtle emergent complex interactions. Although systems work safely individually, unforeseen interactions expose organisations to new classes of socio-technical hazards hardly considered in individual risk analysis. The paper points out how complex domains like healthcare would benefit from risk analysis. However, it stresses about how healthcare organisational issues and culture pose new challenges for system designers.

137. Williams R, Edge D. The social shaping of technology. *Res Policy*, 25(6): 865–899, 1996.

The paper reviews relevant research work that defines the Social Shaping of Technology (SST). It discusses how diverse factors (e.g. social, economical and technical) drive the design and implementation of technology. Moreover, it advocates that a technology policy agenda should benefit from the key aspects characterising STT.

138. Williams R, Stewart J, Slack R. *Social Learning in Technological Innovation: Experimenting with Information and Communication Technologies.* Edward Elgar, 2005.

The book defines a framework of *Social Learning* for the analysis and characterisation of technological innovation processes emerging in Information and Communication Technologies. The frame pinpoints the processes of *learning by doing*, emphasising the acquisition of past experiences, and *learning by interacting*, emphasising the knowledge acquisition by social interactions. The framework allows the revision of engineering and innovation processes. It, furthermore, analyses technology adoption, in particular, processes of *innofusion* and *domestication*. The book, finally, develops policy implications for technology innovation according to social learning.

139. Woods DD, Cook RI. Nine steps to move forward from error. *Cogn Technol Work*, 4(2):137–144, 2002.

The paper draws on generalisations of failures of complex systems. It identifies "nine steps to move forward from failure", which constitute a check-list for understanding 'human errors' in complex organisational settings. In particular, it emphasises how often the preliminary conclusions and blame over human errors correspond to a lack of in-depth investigation of the failure's causes. Moreover, it stresses the necessity of understanding contingencies between work practice and technology. It highlights how often change corresponds to increasing pressure over safety and performance, and, consequently, increasing coupling and complexity of cognitive demands. It stresses how safety culture requires organisations to identify suitable feedback mechanisms, which, one the one hand, allow proper investigation of failures, on the other hand, introduce resilient mechanisms enabling organisational learning.

140. World Health Organization (WHO). *Report for the Consultation Meeting on the WHO Business Plan for Classifications*, final report edition, 2004.

The document is the final report of the consultation meeting for the discussions on the WHO business plan for the future development of the WHO classifications. Among the many points discussed are the correction of the "information paradox" and linking classifications to terminologies. The former needs to reduce the information gap affecting the most vulnerable countries. The proposed strategies intend to simplify the subtle complexity of using classifications, e.g. by the adoption of a Short Mortality List (SML). The latter intends to support the development of e-health records and to enable knowledge-based healthcare. The report resumes and discusses all points in the WHO business plan.

141. World Health Organization (WHO). *History of the development of the ICD*, 2011.

This document provides an historical account of the development of the International Classification of Diseases (ICD), from the early attempts to "classify diseases systematically" in the early eighteenth century to the preparations for the revision of the current tenth version of the ICD (ICD-10).

142. World Heath Organization (WHO). *World Health Organization—Family of International Classifications*, June 2004.

The document describes the WHO Family of International Classifications (WHO-FIC), which consists of the *Reference*—e.g. the International Classification of Diseases (ICD)—*Derived* and *Related Classifications*. The document also describes a two-dimension matrix, which enables the management of the family of classifications. The matrix relates *a conceptual framework of the health system and factors influencing health* together with *areas of application*. The combination of the two dimensions "should give rise to mutually exclusive domains". Moreover, the document describes the *principles* underlying the WHO-FIC and its applicability. The document also describes the process for updating and proposing a classification. The health and health related classifications matrix enables the WHO-FIC and its maintenance.

143. World Heath Organization (WHO). *WHO Business Plan for Classifications*, version 1.0 edition, 2005.

The document describes the business plan for the future development of the WHO *Family of International Classifications* (WHO-FIC). It describes the main assets of the WHO-FIC and identifies the major priorities for future developments. Central to the future development of the WHO-FIC is the revision of the current (tenth) version of the *International Classification of Diseases* (ICD). Another priority is concerned with addressing the "information paradox". The objective is to close (reduce) the gap of available information about specific countries. Unfortunately, the most vulnerable countries are the least informed about diseases. This constitutes a major obstacle in monitoring diseases and providing healthcare services. The document stresses how technology plays a critical role in enabling future healthcare services, in particular, in the creation of an e-health record linking terminologies to classifications. This intends to increase comparability across countries. Moreover, another objective is to move from simple statistical accounts of diseases to knowledge-based healthcare. Finally, for each of the major aspects that articulate the future development of the WHO-FIC, the document presents brief risk-benefit analyses.

144. Wright PC, Fields RE, Harrison MD. Analyzing human-computer interaction as distributed cognition: The resource model. *Hum-Comput Interact*, 15(1):1–41, 2000.

The paper defines the "Resources Model" for analysing *Human-Computer Interaction* (HCI). The model articulates *Distributed Cognition* (DC) in order to inform the analysis and evaluation of Human-Computer Interaction. The model consists of *information structures* and *interaction strategies*. Information structures, i.e. Plans, Goals, Possibilities, History, Action-effected relations and States, capture abstract artifacts which allow the characterisation of resources (e.g. knowledge) in human-computer interaction. A "cyclic model of interaction" allows the configuration and use of available resources. On the other hand, interaction strategies (i.e. Plan Following, Goal Construction, Goal Matching, and History-Based Selection and Elimination) identify processes that use available resources. The paper finally discusses some examples, drawn from relevant literature, about how to use the resources model to analyse and design interaction.

Further Reading

Other books supported by DIRC, the *Interdisciplinary Research Collaboration in Dependability*, are:

- Denis Besnard, Cristina Gacek and Cliff B Jones (Eds.). Structure for Dependability: Computer-Based Systems from an Interdisciplinary Perspective, Springer-Verlag, 2006.
- Karen Clarke, Gillian Hardstone, Mark Rouncefield and Ian Sommerville (Eds.). Trust in Technology: A Socio-Technical Perspective, Computer Supported Co-operative Work, volume 36, Springer, 2006.
- Luciana D'Adderio. Inside the Virtual Product: How Organizations Create Knowledge through Software. Edward Elgar Publishing, 2004.
- Donald MacKenzie. Mechanizing Proof: Computing, Risk, and Trust. The MIT Press, 2001.
- Donald MacKenzie. An Engine, Not a Camera: How Financial Models Shape Markets. The MIT Press, 2006.

S. Anderson and M. Felici, *Emerging Technological Risk*,
DOI: 10.1007/978-1-4471-2143-5, © Springer-Verlag London Limited 2012

Author Index

A

Ackerman, M.S., 13, 14, 31, 32, 37, 42, 44, 63
Adam, B., 16
Anderson, R., 17, 21, 62, 64, 67, 85, 86
Anderson, S., 40, 42–44, 83, 120
Arlat, J., 5, 6, 11
Atkinson, C., 13
Aven, T., 4
Avižienis, A., 5, 11, 30, 52

B

Büscher, M., 54–58
Baxter, G., 82
Beck, U., 16–20, 22, 29, 115
Bernstein, T., 18
Besnard, D., 82
Bishop, P., 69, 70
Blanquart, J.-P., 5, 6, 11
Bloomfield, R., 35, 69, 70
Bonss, W., 17
Borodzicz, E.P., 22
Bottitta, S., 15
Bowker, G.C., 16, 29–32, 37, 63, 81, 82
Bruseberg, A., 57

C

Churchill, E.F., 82, 83
Clement, T., 69, 70
Constant, E.W. II, 13
Costes, A., 5, 6, 11
Coulter, N., 30
Crouzet, Y., 5, 6, 11

D

D'Adderio, L., 13, 14, 33, 37, 38, 40, 42–44
Deswarte, Y., 5, 6, 11
Douglas, M., 7, 10, 15, 16, 19, 20, 22, 30, 31, 51, 82, 83, 115

E

Edge, D., 11
Eldabi, T., 13

F

Fabre, J.-C., 5, 6, 11
Felici, M., 15, 22, 60, 62, 64, 66, 67, 72, 73, 74, 77, 83, 115, 120
Fields, R.E., 82
Frewer, L., 16

G

Gigerenzer,G., 16, 88
Greathead, D., 82
Guerra, S., 69, 70
Guillermain, H., 5, 6, 11
Gurr, C., 38

H

Halverson, C.A., 13, 14, 16, 31, 37, 42, 44, 58, 63, 81, 83
Hardstone, G., 33, 37, 38, 40, 42–44, 56
Harrison, M.D., 71, 72, 82
Hartswood, M., 42, 54–58
Hollnagel, E., 15, 16, 52

S. Anderson and M. Felici, *Emerging Technological Risk*,
DOI: 10.1007/978-1-4471-2143-5, © Springer-Verlag London Limited 2012

H (*cont.*)
Hughes, A.C., 5, 11, 52, 54, 60, 61, 69
Hughes, T.P., 5, 11, 30, 52,
    54, 60, 61, 69

J
Johnson, C., 5, 7, 15, 30, 69, 72
Jones, C., 69, 70

K
Küster Filipe, J., 83
Kaâniche, M., 5, 6, 11
Kanoun, K., 5, 6, 11
Kaptelinin, V., 82
Klein, H.K., 82
Kleinman, D.L., 82
Kristensen, V., 4
Kuhn, D.R., 4, 59

L
Löfstedt, R.E., 16
Landwehr, C., 5, 11, 30, 52
Laprie, J.-C., 5, 6, 11, 30, 52
Latour, B., 17, 81, 82, 86, 89
Lau, C., 17
Le Coze, J., 22, 23, 115, 116
Leveson, N.G., 5, 6, 7, 70, 71
Licoppe, C., 82
Littlewood, B., 35, 70, 71
Lutters, W.G., 32

M
MacKenzie, D., 5, 11, 12, 17, 78, 20,
    51, 52, 53, 59, 60, 61, 66, 69,
    81–89, 119
Mazet, C., 5, 6, 11
Millo, Y., 87–89, 119
Mogensen, P., 56, 57
Moore, T., 17, 21, 85, 86
Mythen, G., 16

N
Nardi, B.A., 16, 82, 83
Neumann, P.G., 4, 22, 30, 59, 83, 115
Norman, D.A., 10, 16, 51, 81

O
O'Leary, M., 13

P
Paul, R.J., 13
Perrow, C., 6–8, 12, 15, 19, 20, 22,
    32, 52, 115
Petroski, H., 9, 11, 32, 51, 52
Pidgeon, N., 13
Popov, P., 35, 70
Pouloudi, A., 13
Powell, D., 5, 6, 11
Procter, R., 40, 42–44, 54–58

R
Rabéjac, C., 5, 6, 11
Randell, B., 5, 11, 30, 52
Reason, J., 16, 20
Rees, G., 42, 56
Rizzo, A., 4, 30
Robertson, B., 39
Rogers, Y., 4, 30
Rouchy, P., 54–58
Rouncefield, M., 54–58
Rushby, J., 82

S
Scaife, M., 4, 30
Schwarz, H., 16, 82, 83
Shapiro, D., 56, 57
Slack, R., 11, 42, 52, 54–58, 82
Slovic, P., 7, 15, 20, 21
Smith, S.P., 71, 72
Smoreda, Z., 82
Sommerville, I., 54
Soutter, J., 57
Sribar, V., 39
Star, S.L., 16, 29, 30, 31, 32, 37,
    63, 81, 82
Stewart, J., 11, 52, 82, 83
Storey, N., 5, 20, 69, 70, 71
Strigini, L., 35, 70
Strum, S., 81, 82, 86, 89

T
Thevenod, P., 5, 6, 11
Todd, P.M., 16, 88

V
Van Loon, J., 16
Vincenti, W.G., 8–10, 13, 31, 32, 37, 51–53,
    59, 61, 66, 68
Voss, A., 42, 54–58

W
Wajcman, J., 11, 51, 53, 59, 60, 61, 66, 81–83
Wallace, D.R., 4, 59
Whittaker, S., 16, 82, 83
Wildavsky, A., 7, 10, 15, 16, 19, 20, 22, 30,
        31, 51, 82, 83, 115

Williams, R., 11, 33, 37, 38, 40, 42–44, 52, 57,
        58, 82
Wright, D., 30, 70, 71, 82
Wright, P., 82

Subject Index

A

Absolute rationality, 8
Accident, 5–8, 15, 19, 54, 73, 76, 86, 97, 115
  definition, 6
Accountability, 20, 42, 43, 46, 57
Accuracy, 40
ACM Computing Classification System, 30
Activity Theory, 82, 100
Actor-Network Theory (ANT), 82, 86, 87
Air Navigation Service Providers
  (ANSPs), 20
Air Traffic Control (ATC), 15, 81
Air Traffic Management (ATM), 52, 72, 74, 77
Anti-lock Braking System (ABS), 15
As Low As Reasonably Possible
  (ALARP), 20
Austinian performativity
  see performativity, 86
Automotive, 16, 37
Availability, 6
Average Number of Requirements
  Changes, 64
Avionics, 15, 52, 62, 64, 67, 81

B

Barnesian performativity
  see performativity, 18
Barriers, 13, 108
Black-Scholes-Merton
  see option pricing, 87
Boundary Hazards, 24, 33, 44–46, 83, 95, 96,
  105, 107, 109, 117, 118, 220
Boundary Infrastructures, 81, 99, 32,
  35, 46, 47

Boundary Objects, 29, 31, 32, 34, 36–40,
  42–47, 51, 55, 75, 81–83, 89,
  96–100, 103, 106, 117–119
Bounded rationality, 7, 16, 88, 100, 105

C

Calculability, 20, 97
Capital Asset Pricing Model, 87
Causal analysis, 5, 30
Change management, 52
Changes, 11, 19, 22, 35, 36, 46, 54, 55,
  60, 62, 64–68, 72–74, 78, 99,
  101, 104–106
  history, 65
Civil Aviation Authorities, 20
Classification systems
  see classifications
Classifications, 7, 22, 23, 29, 30, 31, 32, 40,
  44, 45, 63, 65, 115, 116
Co-realisation
Commercial-Off-The-Shelf (COTS), 36, 37,
  40, 42, 45, 47, 565, 57, 69, 70,
  75, 117
Communities of practice, 12, 13, 14, 16, 31,
  34, 33, 34, 37, 38, 39, 40, 42, 44, 46,
  47, 51, 53, 54, 55, 56, 57, 58, 59, 61,
  63, 64, 65, 75, 81, 82, 89, 96, 97, 98,
  99, 100, 101, 103, 104, 105, 106,
  107, 108, 109, 116, 118, 119, 121
Completeness, 40
Complex interactions, 7, 8, 22, 72, 73, 75,
  77, 115
  see interactions, 7
  definition, 7

S. Anderson and M. Felici, *Emerging Technological Risk*,
DOI: 10.1007/978-1-4471-2143-5, © Springer-Verlag London Limited 2012

C (*cont.*)

Complexity, 7, 8, 15, 16, 19, 22, 32, 52, 60, 70,
    75, 101, 102, 103, 106, 115
Compositionality, 70
Computer Aided Detection (CAD), 101, 102,
    103
Computer-based systems
    see socio-technical systems
Confidence, 5, 15, 103, 70, 71
Confidentiality, 6
Contextualisation, 14, 32, 35, 38, 44,
    100, 103
    decontextualisation, 14, 37, 38, 44,
        100, 103
    recontextualisation
Correctness, 70
Counterperformativity
    see performativity, 18
Coupling, 7, 8, 15, 16, 30, 31, 32, 46, 52, 55,
    62, 74, 75, 100, 104, 118
Cultural Theory, 19, 20, 21, 83
Culture, 6, 7, 12, 13, 19, 20, 21, 35, 38, 39, 47,
    56, 57, 73, 87
Cumulative Number of Requirements
    Changes (CR_C), 64

D

Decontextualisation
    see contextualisation, 44
Dependability, 5, 6, 11, 52, 58, 60, 69, 70, 72,
    75, 76, 82, 89, 90, 95, 96, 104, 105,
    106, 107, 108, 109, 118, 119, 121,
    32, 35, 39, 43, 45
    definition, 5
Dependencies, 30, 66, 67, 68, 71, 73, 75,
    85, 101
DEPOSE systems, 7
Design knowledge
    see knowledge
DIRC
Distributed Cognition, 10, 16, 42, 51, 81, 82,
    88, 100
Diversity, 34, 35, 46, 47, 70, 75, 84, 87, 89,
    90, 96, 101, 102, 103, 116, 118,
    119, 120
Divisions of labour, 19, 20, 37, 40, 42, 43, 45,
    46, 54, 57, 65, 73, 75, 76, 96, 98,
    105, 106, 117, 118, 120
Domestication
    see Social Learning, 82
DOPE, 105, 106

E

E-health, 30
Economics, 17, 18, 21, 84, 85, 86, 87, 89,
    118, 119
Effective performativity
    see performativity, 18
Efficient market hypothesis, 85
Electronic Medical Record (EMR), 98, 99
Engineering knowledge
    see knowledge
Engineering learning process, 9
Errors, 6, 11, 13, 14, 15, 30, 52, 95, 101
Evolution, 4, 11, 12, 13, 22, 40, 51, 52, 53, 54,
    59, 60, 61, 62, 63, 65, 66, 67, 69, 70,
    73, 74, 75, 76, 77, 81, 83, 101, 118
Evolutionary drivers, 10, 51
Evolutionary Hazards, 24, 53, 74, 75, 76, 95,
    96, 100, 104, 105, 107, 109, 117,
    118, 120
Externalisation, 82

F

Failure independence, 72, 101
Failures, 5, 6, 8, 11, 14, 15, 22, 23, 30, 32,
    39, 51, 52, 56, 58, 59, 60, 69, 72,
    73, 74, 75, 76, 78, 83, 84, 89, 90,
    95, 96, 99, 101, 103, 104, 107,
    115, 116, 118, 119
    common-mode
    functional, 10, 11, 13, 51
False negative, 101
False positive, 101, 105, 106
Fault tolerance, 35
Fault-free argument, 70
Faults, 6, 11, 30, 38, 52, 70, 82
Financial markets, 84–89, 119
Functional failures
    see failures, 10

G

Generic performativity
    see performativity, 18

H

Hazard and Operability Analysis (HAZOP), 70
Hazards, 8, 14, 17, 20, 21, 22, 23, 24, 32, 33,
    35, 43, 45, 53, 54, 56, 57, 58, 69, 76,
    77, 83, 84, 89, 90, 95, 96, 107, 108,
    109, 115, 116, 117, 119, 120, 121

see Boundary Hazards,
    see Evolutionary Hazards,
    see Performativity Hazards, 90
definition, 5
hazard analysis, 71, 72
Healthcare, 20, 39, 40, 42, 45, 56, 95, 96, 109
Heterogeneous engineering, 11, 12, 14, 53,
    61, 62
Heuristics, 16, 105
High Reliability Theory (HRT), 7
Historical Requirements Maturity Index
    (*HRMI*), 64
Human cognition, 16, 81, 82
Human errors, 14, 15, 95, 96
Human factors, 22, 57, 81
Human Reliability Analysis (HRA), 16
Human-Computer Interaction (HCI), 95
Human-Machine Interaction (HMI), 15, 101

I
ICD-10, 10, 29
ICD-11, 11, 30
IEC 61508, 5
Incident, 6, 7, 77, 105, 106
    definition, 6
INDEED
Individualism, 19, 87
Information, 8, 13, 16, 18, 21, 22, 29, 30,
    31, 37, 40, 41, 42, 43, 44, 45, 47,
    60, 63, 64, 65, 66, 67, 75, 77, 81,
    85, 86, 88, 90, 95, 97, 99, 101,
    105, 106, 117, 118
difficulties, 13
ecology, 16
loss of information, 83
paradox, 30
Information Society (IS), 17, 29, 81, 82,
    107, 108
Innofusion
    see Social Learning, 82
Innovation, 4, 9–14, 17, 18, 21, 23, 2430, 33,
    37, 38, 40, 44, 45, 51–60, 68, 68, 73,
    75–77, 81, 83, 90, 95, 96, 98–100,
    104, 107–109, 116, 118, 120, 121
Integrity, 6, 40
Interactions, 11, 13, 14, 22, 32, 37, 52, 54, 59,
    61, 64, 70, 72, 73, 75, 77, 82, 84, 85,
    86, 88–90, 95, 97–104, 106–109,
    116, 118–120
Interdisciplinarity, 4
Interdisciplinary, 4, 22–24, 116, 117

Internalisation, 82
International Classification of Diseases (ICD)
    ICD-10, 29
    ICD-11, 30
Investigations, 5, 22, 23, 57, 58, 60, 67, 82,
    85, 87, 95, 104, 105, 115, 116,
    120, 33, 46

K
Knowledge, 7–16, 19–22, 29, 30, 32–34,
    37–39, 44–47, 51–58, 60, 61, 63,
    64, 66, 68, 69, 71–78, 83, 85, 86,
    88, 96–101, 103–106, 109, 115,
    117, 118, 120
descriptive, 10, 32
explicit, 10, 31
growth, 9, 10, 11, 51, 59, 60, 64, 67, 68
management, 96–98
prescriptive, 10
procedural, 10, 11, 31, 32, 37
tacit, 10
transfer of knowledge, 14, 33–36, 45, 46
Kripke models, 66, 74

L
Lack of trust
    see trust, 46
Learning by doing, 11, 52, 545
Learning by interacting, 11, 52, 82
Learning by mistakes, 11
Linear interactions, 7
    see interactions, 7
    definition, 7
Liveness, 66
Long Term Capital Management
    (LTCM), 84, 85, 87
Loss of information
    see information

M
Maintainability, 6
Man-made disasters model, 13
Management Information System (MIS), 97
Manufacturing, 14, 57, 33, 34, 37
Membership, 31, 32, 39, 54, 55, 57, 82,
    99, 108
Mistrust
    see trust
Modalities, 66

M (*cont.*)
Modern state, 29
Modernisation, 17, 20
    re-modernisation, 17
    reflexive modernisation, 18
Multidisciplinarity, 4

N
N-type, 85, 89
Naturalisation, 31–33, 39, 54–56, 82, 108
Neonatal Intensive Care Unit (NICU), 104, 105
Normal Accident Theory (NAT), 7
Normal design, 9

O
Option pricing
    Black-Scholes-Merton, 87
    equation, 87
    theory, 84, 88
Organisational boundaries, 19, 20, 23, 31, 32,
    35, 40, 42–47, 57, 65, 73, 75, 76, 83,
    96, 98, 106, 116–118, 120
Organisational culture
    see culture, 57
Organisational forgetting, 63
Organisational knowledge
    see knowledge
Organisational learning, 13, 63, 106
Organisational memory, 14, 63, 96, 31, 37,
    38, 42
Overtrust
    see trust, 15

P
Patient Information Management System
    (PIMS), 40, 42
Performance, 10–12, 15, 16, 19, 36, 39, 40, 42,
    43, 51, 52, 56–58, 64, 97, 99, 101–104
Performativity, 17, 18, 83–90, 119
    Austinian, 86
    Barnesian, 18, 84
    counterperformativity, 18, 84, 86, 89, 119
    effective, 18, 84
    generic, 18, 84, 86
    limitations, 86–89, 119
Performativity Hazards, 24, 89, 90, 95, 96,
    109, 117, 119, 120
Presumptive anomaly, 10, 13, 51, 52
Probabilistic risk assessment, 19
Propositional Modal Logic, 66
Psychometric Paradigm, 21

R
Radical design, 9
Random walk model, 85
Re-modernisation
    see modernisation, 17
Recontextualisation
    see contextualisation, 44
Redundancy, 75, 118
Reflexive modernisation
    see modernisation, 18
Reflexivity, 17
Reliability, 4–6, 15, 34, 58, 60, 70, 75, 101
Requirements, 4, 10, 11, 13, 31, 51–53, 56, 58,
    61–64, 66–68, 105
    changes, 60–68
    dependencies, 66–68
    evolution, 60–63, 65–67
    management, 66
    traceability, 62, 66
    viewpoints, 61
Requirements engineering, 60, 61
Requirements Maturity Index (RMI), 64
Requirements Stability Index (RSI)
Resilience, 14, 75, 84, 87, 89, 96, 118, 120
Responsibilities, 40, 42–44, 46, 47, 54–58, 65,
    75, 76, 8, 83, 96, 99, 106, 118, 120
Reusability, 69
Reverse salient, 60
Risk, 3–8, 10, 12, 13, 15–24, 30–32, 38, 43,
    46, 51, 52, 54–58, 60, 67–69, 71,
    75–77, 83, 84, 85, 86, 87, 88, 89, 90,
    95, 96, 107, 108, 109, 115, 116,
    117, 118, 119, 120, 121
    analysis, 3, 7, 24, 77, 95, 96, 107, 109, 117,
        120, 121
    definition, 5
    management, 18, 56, 83
    perception, 7, 8, 12, 13, 15, 19, 20, 21, 52,
        58, 82, 83, 88, 107
    social-amplification, 20
Risk homeostasis, 15, 52
Risk Society, 4, 16, 17, 18, 19, 20, 22, 29, 115
Robustness, 14, 35, 84, 87

S
S-loops, 85, 86
S-type, 85, 89
Safety, 4, 5, 6, 12, 15, 23, 35, 52, 60, 66, 69,
    70, 72, 73, 74, 75, 77, 78, 101, 115
    analysis, 71, 72, 74, 76, 77, 78
    climate, 20
    culture, 13, 20
    safety cases, 69, 70, 72, 73, 74, 77, 78

safety-critical, 5, 52, 69, 70, 71, 72, 73
Scalability, 66
Security, 17, 21, 60, 85
    standards, 21, 30, 31, 32, 33, 45, 47, 63, 69,
        77, 117
Security risk assessment, 21
Sensitivity, 16, 19, 101, 102, 103, 106
SHEL model, 81
Short Mortality List (SML), 30
Social connectivity, 81, 88, 89, 90, 96, 99, 107,
        108, 119, 120
Social interactions
    see interactions
Social Learning, 11, 52, 82
    domestication, 82
    innofusion, 82
Social networks, 16, 20, 82, 83, 85, 86, 87, 89,
        90, 96, 107, 108, 119
Social Shaping of Technology (SST), 11, 12,
        14, 16, 51, 53, 59, 60, 61, 66, 81, 83,
        96, 108, 120
Social structures
    see social networks, 20
Socio-technical hazards
    see hazards
Socio-technical systems, 3, 11, 15, 16, 24, 60,
        62, 81, 82, 83, 84, 89, 90, 101, 104,
        117, 119
Software architecture, 5, 62, 68
Software Criticality Analysis (SCA), 69, 70
Software engineering, 54, 70
Software releases, 62, 64
Software Requirements Specification
        (SRS), 62
Specificity, 101, 102
Standardisation, 33, 34, 35, 36, 40, 42, 45, 46,
        55, 118
Standards, 21, 30, 31, 32, 33, 45, 47, 63, 69,
        77, 117
Swiss Cheese Model, 20
System Approach, 11, 52, 54, 61
System flaws
    see faults

T
Threats
    see hazards, 22
Timeliness, 40, 66
Traceability
    see requirements traceability, 66
Trajectories, 11, 12, 31, 37, 42, 44, 52, 53, 56,
        59, 60, 61, 62, 63, 67, 69, 71, 72, 74,

        75, 76, 77, 83, 96, 99, 100, 104, 105,
        106, 107, 118, 120
Trust, 5, 6, 15, 43, 45, 46, 55, 56, 57, 58,
        69, 73, 75, 76, 83, 86, 87, 88,
        99, 101, 103
    lack of trust, 35, 36, 43, 46, 73
    mistrust, 35, 46, 57, 58, 65, 75, 83,
        86, 87, 88, 96, 118, 120
    mutual trust
    overtrust, 15, 103, 106
    trustworthiness, 69

U
Uncertainty, 8, 9, 10, 13, 20, 51, 52, 74, 78,
        102, 103, 105
Undependabilities, 14, 35, 44, 45, 59,
        89, 96, 104
Unknown risk
    see risk, 8

V
Validity, 40, 66, 71, 72
Variation-selection model, 51, 9
Victims, 8
    first-party victims, 8
    fourth-party victims, 8
    second-party victims, 8
    third-party victims, 8
Volatility, 54, 67
Vulnerabilities, 10, 17, 23, 30, 89, 90, 95, 116,
        119, 120

W
WHO Family of International
        Classifications, 29
Work practices, 12, 13, 15, 23, 31, 34, 35, 36,
        37, 38, 39, 43, 44, 45, 46, 47, 52, 54,
        55, 56, 57, 58, 59, 60, 62, 63, 65, 67,
        73, 74, 75, 76, 83, 90, 97, 98, 99,
        100, 101, 102, 104, 105, 106, 107,
        116, 117, 118
World Health Organization (WHO), 29, 30

X
XML (Extensible Markup Language), 30

Y
Y2K, 20